Reading STREET

Grade 2

Scott Foresman

Weekly Tests
Teacher's Manual

PEARSON

Glenview, Illinois • Boston, Massachusetts • Chandler, Arizona • Upper Saddle River, New Jersey

The Pearson Promise

As the largest educational publishing company in the world, Pearson is committed to providing you with curriculum that not only meets the Common Core State Standards, but also supports your implementation of these standards with your students.

Pearson has aligned the Common Core State Standards to every grade level of *Scott Foresman Reading Street,* our premier educational curriculum. This product provides an alignment of the Common Core State Standards to the Grade 2 assessment items in *Scott Foresman Reading Street Weekly Tests.*

We value your partnership highly and look forward to continuing our mission to provide educational materials that fully satisfy your classroom needs.

Copyright © Pearson Education, Inc., or its affiliates. All Rights Reserved. Printed in the United States of America. This publication is protected by copyright, and permission should be obtained from the publisher prior to any prohibited reproduction, storage in a retrieval system, or transmission in any form or by any means, electronic, mechanical, photocopying, recording, or likewise. The publisher hereby grants permission to reproduce these pages, in part or in whole, for classroom use only, the number not to exceed the number of students in each class. Notice of copyright must appear on all copies. For information regarding permissions, write to Pearson Curriculum Group Rights & Permissions, One Lake Street, Upper Saddle River, New Jersey 07458.

Pearson, Scott Foresman, and Pearson Scott Foresman are trademarks, in the U.S. and/or other countries, of Pearson Education, Inc., or its affiliates.

ISBN-13: 978-0-328-68131-0
ISBN-10:   0-328-68131-8
7 8 9 10 V001 15 14 13

CONTENTS

Unit 4 Our Changing World

Unit 5 Responsibility

Unit 6 Traditions

OVERVIEW

The Weekly Tests are an important part of the wide array of formal tests and classroom assessments that support instruction in Scott Foresman *Reading Street*. These tests are designed to measure children's progress based on the vocabulary, phonics, word analysis, and comprehension skills taught each week. Progress on the Weekly Tests is critical for determining whether the child is mastering the weekly target skills.

This Teacher's Manual includes the following: (1) a description of the Weekly Tests, (2) instructions for administering the tests, (3) instructions for scoring and recording test results, (4) reproducible charts on which to track children's progress, (5) the answers to the tests, and (6) alignments to the Common Core State Standards (in the Item Analysis charts and at the bottom of each student test page).

DESCRIPTION OF THE WEEKLY TESTS

In Grade 2, there are 30 tests—one for each week in the Scott Foresman *Reading Street* program.

Each test contains 4 subtests:

- The **Vocabulary** subtest consists of 5 multiple-choice questions that assess children's knowledge of the week's selection vocabulary words.

- The **Phonics/Word Analysis** subtest consists of 5 multiple-choice questions that assess children's understanding of the week's phonics or word analysis skill.

- The **Comprehension** subtest consists of a reading passage and 5 multiple-choice questions that assess the week's target comprehension skill.

- The **Writing** subtest consists of a writing prompt that asks children to respond to the main selection in the Student Edition.

ADMINISTERING THE WEEKLY TESTS

The weekly tests should be administered at the end of Day 5 in each week.

These tests are not intended to be timed. However, for the purposes of scheduling, planning, and practicing for timed-test situations, the tests can be administered in 45 minutes—approximately 15 minutes for the Vocabulary and Word Analysis subtests, 15 minutes for the Comprehension subtest, and 15 minutes for the Writing subtest.

SCORING THE WEEKLY TESTS

Answer keys for the Weekly Tests begin on page 1. Refer to the answer key for the test you are scoring and mark each multiple-choice question as either correct (1 point) or incorrect (0 points). To score the Writing subtest, refer to the rubrics that begin on page T15.

When you have finished scoring a child's test, complete the appropriate row in the Student Progress Chart and the Class Progress Chart. Doing so allows you to keep track of children's total scores as well as their scores on each of the individual subtests. The chart can also help you monitor children's progress throughout the year.

To assess whether a child has mastered the target comprehension skill on a particular test, look at the number of items the child had correct. If the child missed more than 1 question on the target skill, then the child needs further reteaching and practice. Refer to the Item Analysis chart that begins on page T9 to identify the skills assessed on each test and the Common Core State Standard aligned to each skill.

RETEACHING OPTIONS

If a child performs poorly on a Weekly Test or shows a lack of adequate progress during the year, use the Review Lessons in the Scott Foresman *Reading Street* Teacher's Editions and provide the child with additional opportunities to practice the selection vocabulary and target skills.

Scott Foresman *Reading Street*
Student Weekly Test Progress Chart—Grade 2

Name: _____

Test	Vocabulary	Phonics/Word Analysis	Comprehension	TOTAL
Weekly Test 1	/5	/5	/5	/15
Weekly Test 2	/5	/5	/5	/15
Weekly Test 3	/5	/5	/5	/15
Weekly Test 4	/5	/5	/5	/15
Weekly Test 5	/5	/5	/5	/15
Weekly Test 6	/5	/5	/5	/15
Weekly Test 7	/5	/5	/5	/15
Weekly Test 8	/5	/5	/5	/15
Weekly Test 9	/5	/5	/5	/15
Weekly Test 10	/5	/5	/5	/15
Weekly Test 11	/5	/5	/5	/15
Weekly Test 12	/5	/5	/5	/15
Weekly Test 13	/5	/5	/5	/15
Weekly Test 14	/5	/5	/5	/15
Weekly Test 15	/5	/5	/5	/15
Weekly Test 16	/5	/5	/5	/15
Weekly Test 17	/5	/5	/5	/15
Weekly Test 18	/5	/5	/5	/15
Weekly Test 19	/5	/5	/5	/15
Weekly Test 20	/5	/5	/5	/15
Weekly Test 21	/5	/5	/5	/15
Weekly Test 22	/5	/5	/5	/15
Weekly Test 23	/5	/5	/5	/15
Weekly Test 24	/5	/5	/5	/15
Weekly Test 25	/5	/5	/5	/15
Weekly Test 26	/5	/5	/5	/15
Weekly Test 27	/5	/5	/5	/15
Weekly Test 28	/5	/5	/5	/15
Weekly Test 29	/5	/5	/5	/15
Weekly Test 30	/5	/5	/5	/15

Scott Foresman *Reading Street*
Class Weekly Test Progress Chart—Grade 2

Teacher's Name: _____

Child's Name	1	2	3	4	5	6	7	8	9	10	11	12	13	14	15	16	17	18	19	20	21	22	23	24	25	26	27	28	29	30
														Weekly Test Total Score															
1																														
2																														
3																														
4																														
5																														
6																														
7																														
8																														
9																														
10																														
11																														
12																														
13																														
14																														
15																														
16																														
17																														
18																														
19																														
20																														
21																														
22																														
23																														
24																														
25																														
26																														
27																														
28																														
29																														
30																														

Weekly Tests Teacher's Manual

Weekly Test Item Analysis—Grade 2

TEST	SECTION	ITEMS	SKILL	COMMON CORE STATE STANDARD
Weekly Test 1	**Vocabulary**	1–5	Understand and use new vocabulary	Foundational Skills 3.f.
	Phonics	6–10	Short vowels and consonants	Foundational Skills 3.a.
	Comprehension	11–15	◉ Character and setting	Literature 3.
	Written Response	Look Back and Write	Respond to literature	Literature 3. (Also Literature 1., 7., Language 1., 2., 3.)
Weekly Test 2	**Vocabulary**	1–5	Understand and use new vocabulary	Foundational Skills 3.f.
	Phonics	6–10	Long vowels VCe	Foundational Skills 3.a.
	Comprehension	11–15	◉ Main idea	11, 14, 15: Informational Text 1. 12, 13: Informational Text 2.
	Written Response	Look Back and Write	Respond to literature	Writing 2. (Also Informational Text 3., Language 1., 2., 3.)
Weekly Test 3	**Vocabulary**	1–5	Understand and use new vocabulary	Foundational Skills 3.f.
	Phonics	6–10	Consonant blends	Foundational Skills 3.
	Comprehension	11–15	◉ Character and setting	Literature 3.
	Written Response	Look Back and Write	Respond to literature	Informational Text 3. (Also Writing 2., Language 1., 2.)
Weekly Test 4	**Vocabulary**	1–5	Understand and use new vocabulary	Foundational Skills 3.f.
	Phonics	6–10	Inflected endings	Foundational Skills 3.
	Comprehension	11–15	◉ Main idea	11, 14, 15: Informational Text 2. 12, 13: Informational Text 1.
	Written Response	Look Back and Write	Respond to literature	Writing 2. (Also Informational Text 1., Language 1., 2., 3.)
Weekly Test 5	**Vocabulary**	1–5	Understand and use new vocabulary	Foundational Skills 3.f.
	Phonics	6–10	Consonant digraphs	Foundational Skills 3.
	Comprehension	11–15	◉ Facts and details	Informational Text 1.
	Written Response	Look Back and Write	Respond to literature	Writing 3. (Also Literature 3., Language 1., 2., 3.)

Weekly Test Item Analysis—Grade 2

TEST	SECTION	ITEMS	SKILL	COMMON CORE STATE STANDARD
Weekly Test 6	**Vocabulary**	1–5	Understand and use new vocabulary	Foundational Skills 3.f.
	Phonics	6–10	*r*-controlled vowels *ar, or, ore, oar*	Foundational Skills 3.e.
	Comprehension	11–15	◉ Cause and effect	Informational Text 1.
	Written Response	Look Back and Write	Respond to literature	Literature 1. (Also Language 1., 2.)
Weekly Test 7	**Vocabulary**	1–5	Understand and use new vocabulary	Foundational Skills 3.f.
	Phonics	6–10	Contractions	Foundational Skills 3.
	Comprehension	11–15	◉ Author's purpose	Informational Text 6.
	Written Response	Look Back and Write	Respond to literature	Informational Text 1. (Also Writing 1., 2., 5., Language 1., 2.)
Weekly Test 8	**Vocabulary**	1–5	Understand and use new vocabulary	Foundational Skills 3.f.
	Phonics	6–10	*r*-controlled vowels *er, ir, ur*	Foundational Skills 3.e.
	Comprehension	11–15	◉ Facts and details	Informational Text 1.
	Written Response	Look Back and Write	Respond to literature	Informational Text 1. (Also Writing 2., 5., Language 1., 2.)
Weekly Test 9	**Vocabulary**	1–5	Understand and use new vocabulary	Foundational Skills 3.f.
	Phonics	6–10	Plurals	Foundational Skills 3.e.
	Comprehension	11–15	◉ Cause and effect	Informational Text 3.
	Written Response	Look Back and Write	Respond to literature	Literature 6. (Also Writing 3., 5., Language 1., 2.)
Weekly Test 10	**Vocabulary**	1–5	Understand and use new vocabulary	Foundational Skills 3.f.
	Phonics	6–10	Vowel patterns *a, ai, ay*	Foundational Skills 3.b.
	Comprehension	11–15	◉ Compare and contrast	11–14: Literature 3. 15: Literature 1.
	Written Response	Look Back and Write	Respond to literature	Literature 2. (Also Writing 5., Language 1., 2.)

Weekly Test Item Analysis—Grade 2

TEST	SECTION	ITEMS	SKILL	COMMON CORE STATE STANDARD
Weekly Test 11	**Vocabulary**	1–5	Understand and use new vocabulary	Foundational Skills 3.f.
	Phonics	6–10	Vowels patterns *e, ee, ea, y*	Foundational Skills 3.b.
	Comprehension	11–15	◉ Author's purpose	Informational Text 6.
	Written Response	Look Back and Write	Respond to literature	Writing 3. (Also Language 1.)
Weekly Test 12	**Vocabulary**	1–5	Understand and use new vocabulary	Foundational Skills 3.f.
	Phonics	6–10	Vowels patterns *o, oa, ow*	Foundational Skills 3.b.
	Comprehension	11–15	◉ Draw conclusions/ make inferences	Literature 3.
	Written Response	Look Back and Write	Respond to literature	Writing 3. (Also Literature 3., Language 1.)
Weekly Test 13	**Vocabulary**	1–5	Understand and use new vocabulary	Foundational Skills 3.f.
	Word Analysis	6–10	Compound words	Language 4.d.
	Comprehension	11–15	◉ Compare and contrast	11, 12, 14: Literature 1. 13, 15: Literature 3.
	Written Response	Look Back and Write	Respond to literature	Writing 3. (Also Literature 3., Language 1.)
Weekly Test 14	**Vocabulary**	1–5	Understand and use new vocabulary	Foundational Skills 3.f.
	Phonics	6–10	Vowel patterns *i, e, igh, y*	Foundational Skills 3.a.
	Comprehension	11–15	◉ Sequence	Literature 5.
	Written Response	Look Back and Write	Respond to literature	Literature 3. (Also Writing 3., 5.)
Weekly Test 15	**Vocabulary**	1–5	Understand and use new vocabulary	Foundational Skills 3.f.
	Word Analysis	6–10	Comparative endings *-er, -est*	Foundational Skills 3.d.
	Comprehension	11–15	◉ Fact and opinion	11, 13–14: Informational Text 1. 12, 15: Informational Text 6.
	Written Response	Look Back and Write	Respond to literature	Informational Text 1. (Also Writing 5., Language 1.)

Weekly Test Item Analysis—Grade 2

TEST	SECTION	ITEMS	SKILL	COMMON CORE STATE STANDARD
Weekly Test 16	**Vocabulary**	1–5	Understand and use new vocabulary	Language 4.
	Phonics	6–10	Final syllable -*le*	Foundational Skills 3.
	Comprehension	11–15	⊙ Draw conclusions/ make inferences	Literature 1.
	Written Response	Look Back and Write	Respond to literature	Literature 3. (Also Language 1., 2., 3.)
Weekly Test 17	**Vocabulary**	1–5	Understand and use new vocabulary	Language 4.a.
	Phonics	6–10	Vowels patterns *oo, u*	6, 8, 10: Foundational Skills 3.b. 7, 9: Foundational Skills 3.
	Comprehension	11–15	⊙ Sequence	11–13: Literature 1. 14, 15: Literature 5.
	Written Response	Look Back and Write	Respond to literature	Writing 2. (Also Informational Text 1., 3., Language 1., 2., 3.)
Weekly Test 18	**Vocabulary**	1–5	Understand and use new vocabulary	Language 4.a.
	Phonics	6–10	Diphthongs *ou, ow, oi, oy*	Foundational Skills 3.b.
	Comprehension	11–15	⊙ Fact and opinion	11, 12, 14: Informational Text 1. 13, 15: Informational Text 6.
	Written Response	Look Back and Write	Respond to literature	Writing 2. (Also Informational Text 1., 3., Language 1., 2., 3.)
Weekly Test 19	**Vocabulary**	1–5	Understand and use new vocabulary	Language 4.
	Phonics	6–10	Syllable patterns	6–7, 10: Foundational Skills 3. 8–9: Foundational Skills 3.c.
	Comprehension	11–15	⊙ Plot and theme	11–14: Literature 1. 15: Literature 2.
	Written Response	Look Back and Write	Respond to literature	Literature 3. (Also Literature 1., 2., Language 1., 2., 3.)
Weekly Test 20	**Vocabulary**	1–5	Understand and use new vocabulary	Language 4.a.
	Phonics	6–10	Vowel digraphs *oo, ue, ew*	Foundational Skills 3.b.
	Comprehension	11–15	⊙ Plot and theme	11, 13–15: Literature 1. 12: Literature 2.
	Written Response	Look Back and Write	Respond to literature	Writing 1. (Also Literature 2., 7., Language 1., 2., 3.)

Weekly Test Item Analysis—Grade 2

TEST	SECTION	ITEMS	SKILL	COMMON CORE STATE STANDARD
Weekly Test 21	**Vocabulary**	1–5	Understand and use new vocabulary	Language 4.a.
	Phonics	6–10	Suffixes *-ly, -iful, -er, -or, -ish*	Foundational Skills 3.d.
	Comprehension	11–15	◉ Fact and opinion	Informational Text 1.
	Written Response	Look Back and Write	Respond to literature	Informational Text 6. (Also Writing 5., Language 1., 2.)
Weekly Test 22	**Vocabulary**	1–5	Understand and use new vocabulary	Language 4.a.
	Phonics	6–10	Prefixes *un-, re-, pre-, dis-*	Foundational Skills 3.d.
	Comprehension	11–15	◉ Cause and effect	Informational Text 1.
	Written Response	Look Back and Write	Respond to literature	Literature 1. (Also Writing 5., Language 1., 2.)
Weekly Test 23	**Vocabulary**	1–5	Understand and use new vocabulary	Language 4.
	Phonics	6–10	Consonant patterns *kn, wr, gn, mb*	Foundational Skills 3.
	Comprehension	11–15	◉ Plot and theme	11–14: Literature 1. 15: Literature 2.
	Written Response	Look Back and Write	Respond to literature	Literature 1. (Also Writing 5., Language 1., 2.)
Weekly Test 24	**Vocabulary**	1–5	Understand and use new vocabulary	Language 4.
	Phonics	6–10	Consonant patterns *ph, gh, ck, ng*	Foundational Skills 3.
	Comprehension	11–15	◉ Character and setting	11, 13, 15: Literature 3. 12, 14: Literature 1.
	Written Response	Look Back and Write	Respond to literature	Literature 1. (Also Writing 5., Language 1., 2.)
Weekly Test 25	**Vocabulary**	1–5	Understand and use new vocabulary	Language 4.a.
	Phonics	6–10	Vowel patterns *aw, au, au(gh), al*	Foundational Skills 3.b.
	Comprehension	11–15	◉ Main idea	Informational Text 2.
	Written Response	Look Back and Write	Respond to literature	Literature 1. (Also Writing 5., Language 1., 2.)

Weekly Test Item Analysis—Grade 2

TEST	SECTION	ITEMS	SKILL	COMMON CORE STATE STANDARD
Weekly Test 26	**Vocabulary**	1–5	Understand and use new vocabulary	Language 4.a.
	Phonics	6–10	Inflected endings	Foundational Skills 3.d.
	Comprehension	11–15	◉ Compare and contrast	Literature 3.
	Written Response	Look Back and Write	Respond to literature	Writing 2. (Also Literature 1., Language 1., 2., 3.)
Weekly Test 27	**Vocabulary**	1–5	Understand and use new vocabulary	Language 4.
	Word Analysis	6–10	Abbreviations	Language 2.
	Comprehension	11–15	◉ Author's purpose	11–13: Informational Text 5. 14–15: Informational Text 6.
	Written Response	Look Back and Write	Respond to literature	Writing 2. (Also Literature 1., Language 1., 2., 3.)
Weekly Test 28	**Vocabulary**	1–5	Understand and use new vocabulary	Language 4.a.
	Word Analysis	6–10	Final syllables *-tion, -ture, -ion*	Foundational Skills 3.
	Comprehension	11–15	◉ Draw conclusions/make inferences	11–14: Informational Text 2. 15: Informational Text 5.
	Written Response	Look Back and Write	Respond to literature	Writing 2. (Also Literature 1., Language 1., 2., 3.)
Weekly Test 29	**Vocabulary**	1–5	Understand and use new vocabulary	Language 4.a.
	Word Analysis	6–10	Suffixes *-ness, -less*	Foundational Skills 3.d.
	Comprehension	11–15	◉ Sequence	Informational Text 1.
	Written Response	Look Back and Write	Respond to literature	Writing 2. (Also Informational Text 1., Language 1., 2., 3.)
Weekly Test 30	**Vocabulary**	1–5	Understand and use new vocabulary	Language 4.a.
	Word Analysis	6–10	Prefixes *mis-, mid-*	Foundational Skills 3.d.
	Comprehension	11–15	◉ Facts and details	Informational Text 1.
	Written Response	Look Back and Write	Respond to literature	Writing 2. (Also Literature 1., 3., Writing 3., Language 1., 2., 3.)

COMPREHENSION TARGET SKILL COVERAGE

How can the Weekly Tests predict student success on Unit Benchmark Tests?

Each Unit Benchmark Test, as well as assessing overall student reading ability, concentrates on two skills taught and/or reviewed during the unit by including several questions on those skills. In order to ensure that comprehension target skill can be accurately learned and then tested, students learn each target skill through a combination of being taught and reviewing the skill multiple times before testing occurs. The charts below show the units/weeks where the target comprehension skills are taught and where they are tested on Weekly Tests. Based on the student's number of correct answers for each tested target skill, the teacher will know whether a student has gained the necessary skill knowledge before the Unit Test is given. A low score on the Weekly Tests probably indicates a need for closer review of the student's performance and perhaps additional instruction. It is important to understand that these tests provide only one look at the student's progress and should be interpreted in conjunction with other assessments and the teacher's observation.

Using the Comprehension Target Skill Coverage Chart

To score target skill knowledge, use the Comprehension Target Skill Coverage Chart.

1. Make a copy of the appropriate Comprehension Target Skill Coverage chart for each student.

2. To score, circle the number of correct answers the student had for that skill on the appropriate Weekly Test.

3. Using the total number of correct answers for a skill, check the appropriate box under *Student Trend* to indicate whether or not the student has acquired the target skill knowledge. We recommend 90% correct as the criterion for skill aquisition at this level. Add any notes or observations that may be helpful to you and the student in later instruction.

GRADE 2 — COMPREHENSION TARGET SKILL COVERAGE CHART

Student Name _____

Unit 1 Tested Skills	Weekly Test Locations	Number Correct	Student Trend
Literary Elements: Character/Setting **Common Core State Standards** Literature 1., Literature 3.	Weekly Test 1	0 1 2 3 4 5	____ Skill knowledge acquired ____ Skill needs further review
	Weekly Test 3	0 1 2 3 4 5	
Main Idea and Supporting Details **Common Core State Standards** Informational Text 2.	Weekly Test 2	0 1 2 3 4 5	____ Skill knowledge acquired ____ Skill needs further review
	Weekly Test 4	0 1 2 3 4 5	

Unit 2 Tested Skills	Weekly Test Locations	Number Correct	Student Trend
Compare and Contrast **Common Core State Standards** Literature 1., Literature 3.	Weekly Test 10	0 1 2 3 4 5	____ Skill knowledge acquired ____ Skill needs further review
Cause and Effect **Common Core State Standards** Informational Text 1., Informational Text 3.	Weekly Test 6	0 1 2 3 4 5	____ Skill knowledge acquired ____ Skill needs further review
	Weekly Test 9	0 1 2 3 4 5	

GRADE 2 — COMPREHENSION TARGET SKILL COVERAGE CHART

Student Name _____

Unit 3 Tested Skills	Weekly Test Locations	Number Correct	Student Trend
Sequence **Common Core State Standards** Literature 1., Literature 5.; Informational Text 1.	Weekly Test 14	0 1 2 3 4 5	____ Skill knowledge acquired ____ Skill needs further review
Author's Purpose **Common Core State Standards** Informational Text 6.	Weekly Test 7	0 1 2 3 4 5	____ Skill knowledge acquired ____ Skill needs further review
	Weekly Test 11	0 1 2 3 4 5	

Unit 4 Tested Skills	Weekly Test Locations	Number Correct	Student Trend
Fact and Opinion **Common Core State Standards** Informational Text 1.	Weekly Test 15	0 1 2 3 4 5	____ Skill knowledge acquired ____ Skill needs further review
	Weekly Test 18	0 1 2 3 4 5	
Draw Conclusions **Common Core State Standards** Literature 1., Literature 3.; Informational Text 2.	Weekly Test 12	0 1 2 3 4 5	____ Skill knowledge acquired ____ Skill needs further review
	Weekly Test 16	0 1 2 3 4 5	

GRADE 2 — COMPREHENSION TARGET SKILL COVERAGE CHART

Student Name _____

Unit 5 Tested Skills	Weekly Test Locations	Number Correct	Student Trend
Main Idea and Supporting Details **Common Core State Standards** Informational Text 2.	Weekly Test 2	0 1 2 3 4 5	____ Skill knowledge acquired ____ Skill needs further review
	Weekly Test 4	0 1 2 3 4 5	
	Weekly Test 25	0 1 2 3 4 5	
Cause and Effect **Common Core State Standards** Informational Text 1.	Weekly Test 6	0 1 2 3 4 5	____ Skill knowledge acquired ____ Skill needs further review
	Weekly Test 9	0 1 2 3 4 5	
	Weekly Test 22	0 1 2 3 4 5	

Unit 6 Tested Skills	Weekly Test Locations	Number Correct	Student Trend
Draw Conclusions **Common Core State Standards** Literature 1., Literature 3.; Informational Text 2.	Weekly Test 12	0 1 2 3 4 5	____ Skill knowledge acquired ____ Skill needs further review
	Weekly Test 16	0 1 2 3 4 5	
	Weekly Test 28	0 1 2 3 4 5	
Facts and Details **Common Core State Standards** Informational Text 1.	Weekly Test 5	0 1 2 3 4 5	____ Skill knowledge acquired ____ Skill needs further review
	Weekly Test 8	0 1 2 3 4 5	
	Weekly Test 30	0 1 2 3 4 5	

SCORING RUBRICS FOR WRITING

Use one of the following rubrics (2 points or 4 points depending on your needs) to evaluate responses on the Writing subtest. Suggested top-score responses for each week's prompt follow the rubrics.

Two-Point Scoring Rubric

2 points:

The response indicates that the child has a complete understanding of the reading concept embodied in the task. The response is accurate and complete, and fulfills all the requirements of the task. Necessary support and/or examples are included, and the information given is clearly text-based.

1 point:

The response indicates that the child has a partial understanding of the reading concept embodied in the task. The response includes information that is essentially correct and text-based, but the information is too general or too simplistic. Some of the support and/or examples may be incomplete or omitted.

0 points:

The response indicates that the child does not demonstrate an understanding of the reading concept embodied in the task. The child has either failed to respond or has provided a response that is inaccurate or has insufficient information.

Four-Point Scoring Rubric

4 points:

The response indicates that the child has a thorough understanding of the reading concept embodied in the task. The response is accurate and complete, and fulfills all the requirements of the task. Necessary support and/or examples are included, and the information given is clearly text-based.

3 points:

The response indicates that the child has an understanding of the reading concept embodied in the task. The response is accurate and fulfills all the requirements of the task, but the required support and/or details are not complete or clearly text-based.

2 points:

The response indicates that the child has a partial understanding of the reading concept embodied in the task. The response includes information that is essentially correct and text-based, but the information is too general or too simplistic. Some of the support and/or examples and requirements of the task may be incomplete or omitted.

1 point:

The response indicates that the child has a very limited understanding of the reading concept embodied in the task. The response is incomplete, may exhibit many flaws, and may not address all the requirements of the task.

0 points:

The response indicates that the child does not demonstrate an understanding of the reading concept embodied in the task. The child has either failed to respond or has provided a response that is inaccurate or has insufficient information.

Top-Level Responses

Weekly Test 1:

Top-Score Response A top-score response uses details from the text and the picture to tell what the news is that the boys receive and how they feel about it. For example:

Grandma tells the boys the summer is almost over, and it is time for them to go home. The boys are glad they will be with their families and friends again. The boys are sad they will not be together.

Weekly Test 2:

Top-Score Response A top-score response uses main ideas and details from the text to tell about different jobs astronauts do. For example:

Astronauts do different jobs. Some astronauts fly the space shuttle. Others do experiments with plants.

Weekly Test 3:

Top-Score Response A top-score response uses details from the text and the picture to make inferences about the Big Dipper and the Little Dipper. For example:

The Big Dipper and the Little Dipper are stars in shapes that look like dippers. The campers are pointing to the stars in the night sky when they talk about the Big Dipper and the Little Dipper.

Weekly Test 4:

Top-Score Response A top-score response uses details from the text to describe how a jack rabbit protects itself. For example:

A jack rabbit hears and smells when danger is near. It uses its long legs to escape.

Weekly Test 5:

Top-Score Response A top-score response uses dialogue to write a short play about Little Red Ant talking to a new character. For example:

Little Red Ant: Lizard must be the strongest. I will ask. Lizard, are you the strongest of all?

Lizard: No, I am not the strongest. Roadrunner is stronger. When Roadrunner catches me, he eats me. Here he comes!

Weekly Test 6:

Top-Score Response A top-score response uses details from the text and the picture to tell why Jim believes there is no such thing as a bad dog. For example:

Jim believes there are no bad dogs because he trains dogs and knows that they can learn to be good.

Weekly Test 7:

Top-Score Response A top-score response uses details from the text and the pictures to tell why some people call Abraham Lincoln "America's Great President." For example:

Lincoln is called "America's Great President" because he worked hard with others to put the country back together when it split apart during the Civil War. The armies of the North fought the armies of the South in the Civil War. President Lincoln helped find a way to stop the fighting.

Weekly Test 8:

Top-Score Response A top-score response uses details from the text and the picture to tell why the food company isn't selling juice. For example:

The food company is not selling juice because there is a scarcity of oranges. The cold weather harmed the orange trees so there are fewer oranges. The company makes a trade-off to sell whole oranges.

Weekly Tests Teacher's Manual

Weekly Test 9:

Top-Score Response A top-score response uses details from the text and the pictures to tell how you know who is speaking and create a scene with a new musician. For example:

The name of the character who is speaking is in bold print at the beginning of each piece of dialogue. The Bremen Town Musicians are the donkey, dog, cat, and rooster. As they walked to Bremen they came to a dairy where they met a sad cow.

Cow: Moooo! Moooo!

Donkey: Why are you so sad, cow?

Cow: I can't give any more milk so the dairy farmer doesn't need me anymore.

Dog, Cat, and Rooster: Come with us!

Cow: That's a wonderful idea! Moooooo! Let's go!

Weekly Test 10:

Top-Score Response A top-score response uses details from the text and the picture to tell what the mouse means by "one good turn deserves another." For example:

The mouse set the snake free by moving the rock. The mouse believes that since he did something nice for the snake, the snake should do something nice for him and not eat him.

Weekly Test 11:

Top-Score Response A top-score response uses details from the text and the picture to tell why the talking robot did not win a prize.

The talking robot did not win a prize because it couldn't really talk. The judge found Wagner inside the robot talking in a robot voice.

Weekly Test 12:

Top-Score Response A top-score response uses details from the text and the picture to tell how Juno knew who sent the letter. For example:

Juno saw his name and address on the letter, so he knew it was for him. The red and blue marks on the edges told him the letter was from far away. The special stamp in the corner told him it was from his grandmother.

Weekly Test 13:

Top-Score Response A top-score response uses details from the text and the picture to tell why Anansi does not feel full. For example:

Turtle has tricked Anansi into letting Turtle eat the fish. Anansi hasn't eaten anything so he is not full.

Weekly Test 14:

Top-Score Response A top-score response uses details from the text and the picture to tell how the sisters are alike and different. For example:

Rosa and Blanca are alike because they both planted a garden with the same plants. They are different because Rosa is married with three children while Blanca lives alone.

Weekly Test 15:

Top-Score Response A top-score response uses details from the text to tell why money was not important to George Washington Carver. For example:

George Washington Carver had checks to pay him for work he had done, but he often didn't even cash those checks. Money could not have been important to him.

Weekly Test 16:

Top-Score Response A top-score response uses details from the text to describe the caterpillar's opinion about change. For example:

The caterpillar feels that change is a good thing. He looks forward to changing into a butterfly. He believes that everything in the world changes over time.

Weekly Test 17:

Top-Score Response A top-score response uses details from the text to describe how bees help pumpkin plants. For example:

Bees help pumpkin plants make pumpkins. They do this by carrying pollen on their bodies from male flowers to female flowers. When this happens, the green ball at the end of a female flower begins to grow into a pumpkin.

Weekly Test 18:

Top-Score Response A top-score response uses details from the text to describe what is in soil. For example:

Soil contains bits of rocks and leaves. It also contains plants and small animals.

Weekly Test 19:

Top-Score Response A top-score response uses details from the text to describe what the fish do to help Luna return to the sky. For example:

The fish help Luna return to the night sky. First, they use their fins to gather up bits of the moon. After Luna rolls herself into a ball again, the fish patch and smooth her with their fins. Then they use their scales as glue to hold the pieces together.

Weekly Test 20:

Top-Score Response A top-score response uses details from the text to support their opinion about whether Jade is brave. For example:

I think that Jade is brave. I think this because she is willing to climb the steep mountain to speak to the Mountain Spirit. She doesn't turn back even when boulders fall.

Weekly Test 21:

Top-Score Response A top-score response uses details from the text and the picture to tell why the firefighters are or are not careful as they search for Luke, explains how we know this is not a fictional story, and provides evidence to support answers. For example:

The firefighters are careful as they search for Luke because they wear safety equipment, they feel doors before opening them, and they climb damaged steps slowly. The pictures of the firefighters at the fire show that this story is not fiction.

Weekly Test 22:

Top-Score Response A top-score response uses details from the text and the picture to tell what Carl's petition asks for. For example:

Carl's petition asks the Hanford Town Council to allow the town park to stay open later. The petition includes reasons for changing the park hours, including the kids of Hanford need a good place to play, and grown-ups could stay in the park later, too.

Weekly Test 23:

Top-Score Response A top-score response uses details from the text and the picture to correctly tell what Sam compares Dodger's training to and provides evidence to support the answer. For example:

Sam compares Dodger's training to the spring training baseball players go through. Sam pitches baseballs to Dodger every morning. He teaches him to sit and stay.

Weekly Test 24:

Top-Score Response A top-score response uses details from the text to tell why Dolores changes her mind about the clubhouse and gives evidence to support the answer. For example:

Dolores changes her mind about the girls' clubhouse because she's bored. She wants to go exploring. When the other girls don't agree with her, Dolores quits the club.

Weekly Test 25:

Top-Score Response A top-score response uses details from the text and the picture to tell how Norman fixes the problems he caused, and it provides evidence to support the answer. For example:

Norman fixes the problems he has caused by spending all night painting new signs and putting them up where they belong. He painted and put up stop signs, shop signs, street signs, danger signs, welcome signs, and a sign that says "I'm sorry."

Weekly Test 26:

Top-Score Response A top-score response uses details from the text and the picture to tell how a girl could play baseball like Josh Gibson. For example:

When Danny hurt his arm sliding into second, the team let Grandmama play. She had practiced hitting baseballs with her father when she was little. So she was able to hit the ball hard, catch anything that was thrown, and do everything else that Josh Gibson could do.

Weekly Test 27:

Top-Score Response A top-score response uses details from the text and the picture to explain why Francis Scott Key wrote "The Star-Spangled Banner." For example:

Francis Scott Key wrote "The Star-Spangled Banner" to show his pride. He was watching a battle. British soldiers were attacking an American fort all night long. When the morning came and the flag was still flying, he knew the Americans had won. He was so proud that he wrote "The Star-Spangled Banner."

Weekly Test 28:

Top-Score Response A top-score response uses details from the text and the picture to tell why Cecilia put a flowerpot and a teacup in the basket. For example:

Cecilia put a flowerpot in the basket because she and Tía like to grow flowers. She put a teacup in the basket because Tía makes tea for her when she is sick.

Weekly Test 29:

Top-Score Response A top-score response uses details from the text and the picture to explain how hats protected cowboys. For example:

The wide brim of a cowboy hat kept the sun out of the cowboy's eyes. When it rained, the brim acted like an umbrella and kept the cowboy's face dry.

Weekly Test 30:

Top-Score Response A top-score response uses details from the text and the picture to explain why Grace thought that becoming President was not going to be easy. For example:

Grace thought becoming President was not going to be easy because Thomas was such a good student, and he was good at many things. Grace was worried that the other students would want to vote for him.

Name _____

VOCABULARY

Directions

Read each sentence. Fill in the circle next to the word that fills the blank.

1 We went to the movies _____.

○ friend
○ over
● together

2 Do you live in the _____ or city?

● country
○ night
○ ring

3 Is _____ coming to pick you up?

○ somewhere
● someone
○ room

4 My cat was _____ my bed.

○ most
○ like
● under

5 The paintings in our art show are _____.

○ sort
○ does
● beautiful

GO ON

Common Core State Standards

Questions 1–5: CCSS Foundational Skills 3.f. Recognize and read grade-appropriate irregularly spelled words.

PHONICS

Directions

Read each sentence and the question that follows. Fill in the circle next to the answer.

6 I like to ride at the <u>back</u> of the bus.

Which word has the same sound as <u>a</u> in <u>back</u>?

○ sale
○ name
● cat

7 Rocks usually <u>sit</u> on the bottom of the lake.

Which word has the same sound as <u>i</u> in <u>sit</u>?

○ mine
● tin
○ life

8 I like apples, <u>but</u> grapes are my favorite.

Which word has the same sound as <u>u</u> in <u>but</u>?

○ tuba
○ begin
● number

9 A swan has a long, curvy <u>neck</u>.

Which word has the same sound as <u>e</u> in <u>neck</u>?

● friend
○ neat
○ tiger

10 My mom got a new <u>job</u>.

Which word has the same sound as <u>o</u> in <u>job</u>?

○ boat
○ one
● sock

GO ON

Common Core State Standards

Questions 6–10: CCSS Foundational Skills 3.a. Distinguish long and short vowels when reading regularly spelled one-syllable words.

Weekly Test 1 Unit 1 Week 1

Name _____

COMPREHENSION

A New School

Jamie's family moved to a new town. It was during the summer. That meant Jamie would be going to a new school. He was a little scared. What if he did not like it? He did not have any friends there.

"Do not worry," said Mom.

"You will be fine," said Dad.

"Nobody will like you," said Lisa, his little sister. Jamie was afraid that Lisa was right.

On the first day of school, Jamie got dressed slowly. He ate his breakfast slowly. He walked slowly to the bus stop. He stood there waiting. He was worried.

"Hi," a voice said. "Are you new?" Jamie turned around to see a boy looking at him. The boy was a little taller than Jamie. He had dark hair. He had brown eyes. He smiled at Jamie.

"Yes," Jamie said. "I am Jamie." He smiled at the boy. He was starting to feel better.

"I am Alex," the boy said. "Do you want to be friends?"

Jamie nodded his head. He was going to like his new school!

Directions

Read each question. Fill in the circle next to the best answer.

11 When did Jamie's family move to a new town?

- ○ fall
- ○ winter
- ● summer

12 When Lisa tells Jamie, "Nobody will like you," she is

- ○ being nice.
- ○ telling the truth.
- ● being mean.

13 How does Jamie feel during most of the story?

- ● worried
- ○ happy
- ○ mad

14 Where does Jamie meet Alex?

- ○ at his new house
- ○ at the park
- ● at the bus stop

15 What did Jamie decide after he met Alex?

- ○ He wanted to move again real soon.
- ● He would like his new school.
- ○ He didn't want to ride the bus.

GO ON

Common Core State Standards

Questions 11–15: CCSS Literature 3. Describe how characters in a story respond to major events and challenges.

Name _____

WRITTEN RESPONSE TO THE SELECTION

Look Back and Write Look back at page 33. What is the news the "twins" receive? How do they feel about it? Provide evidence to support your answer.

Use the list in the box below to help you as you write.

REMEMBER—YOU SHOULD

☐ tell what news the "twins" receive and how they feel about it.

☐ use descriptive words to tell how Jorge and Juan feel.

☐ support your ideas with examples from the story.

☐ try to use correct spelling, capitalization, punctuation, grammar, and sentences.

GO ON

Common Core State Standards

CCSS Literature 3. Describe how characters in a story respond to major events and challenges. (Also **CCSS Literature 1.**, **CCSS Literature 7.**, **CCSS Language 1.**, **CCSS Language 2.**, **CCSS Language 3.**)

Name _____

VOCABULARY

Directions
Read each sentence. Fill in the circle next to the word that fills the blank.

1 Stuart spilled paint _____ .
- ⚪ country
- ⚫ everywhere
- ⚪ enough

2 We will _____ to a new town.
- ⚫ move
- ⚪ smell
- ⚪ live

3 Building a house is hard _____ .
- ⚪ beautiful
- ⚪ flower
- ⚫ work

4 That _____ is wearing blue shoes.
- ⚪ nose
- ⚪ food
- ⚫ woman

5 My grandma travels around the _____ .
- ⚪ machines
- ⚪ against
- ⚫ world

GO ON

⌐ **Common Core State Standards** ⌐
Questions 1–5: CCSS Foundational Skills 3.f. Recognize and read grade-appropriate irregularly spelled words.

- -

PHONICS

Directions

Read each sentence and the question that follows. Fill in the circle next to the answer.

6 They sailed in search of <u>spice</u>.

Which word has the same sound as <u>i</u> in <u>spice</u>?

- ○ kick
- ● twice
- ○ police

7 My <u>nose</u> is stuffy today.

Which word has the same sound as <u>o</u> in <u>nose</u>?

- ○ off
- ○ one
- ● hole

8 The mountain we hiked was <u>huge</u>!

Which word has the same sound as <u>u</u> in <u>huge</u>?

- ○ under
- ● use
- ○ stun

9 We played a <u>game</u> after school.

Which word has the same sound as <u>a</u> in <u>game</u>?

- ● race
- ○ barn
- ○ team

10 <u>These</u> are my favorite boots.

Which word has the same sound as <u>e</u> in <u>these</u>?

- ● please
- ○ ten
- ○ check

GO ON

Common Core State Standards

Questions 6–10: **CCSS Foundational Skills 3.a.** Distinguish long and short vowels when reading regularly spelled one-syllable words.

Name _____

COMPREHENSION

Hubble

In 1990 the Hubble Space Telescope was sent into space. A telescope is used to see the stars and planets in outer space. Most telescopes are on Earth. Hubble is special. It is in space.

Hubble circles around Earth. It is about 365 miles above Earth. (Most airplanes fly 4 to 8 miles above Earth.) It goes around Earth in just 97 minutes. It is flying about 5 miles per second. That's 300 miles per minute or 18,000 miles per hour. That's fast! (Big airplanes fly about 500 miles per hour.)

Telescopes are different sizes. Some are small. Some are very big. Hubble is medium-sized. It is about the size of a large school bus. That's big to you and me! It is about 24,000 pounds. That's as heavy as twelve small cars!

People learn a lot from Hubble. They learn about other planets. They learn about stars. They learn about space. Hubble takes pictures. They are very clear. They are better than pictures taken from Earth. These pictures help us learn about the strange and beautiful things around our home planet.

Directions

Read each question. Fill in the circle next to the best answer.

11 Which is a detail from paragraph 1?

- ● Most telescopes are on Earth.
- ○ Hubble goes around Earth in 97 minutes.
- ○ It is medium-sized.

12 What is the main idea of paragraph 2?

- ○ Hubble goes very fast!
- ● Hubble circles around Earth.
- ○ Hubble is faster than an airplane.

13 Hubble is a medium-sized telescope. What is it as big as?

- ○ an airplane
- ○ a planet
- ● a large school bus

14 Which is a detail from paragraph 3?

- ● Hubble is about 24,000 pounds.
- ○ Telescopes are different sizes.
- ○ Hubble is the size of an airplane.

15 What is the main idea of paragraph 4?

- ○ Hubble takes clear pictures.
- ○ People learn about stars.
- ● People learn a lot from Hubble.

GO ON

Common Core State Standards

Questions 11, 14–15: CCSS Informational Text 1. Ask and answer such questions as *who, what, where, when, why,* and *how* to demonstrate understanding of key details in a text. **Questions 12–13: CCSS Informational Text 2.** Identify the main topic of a multiparagraph text as well as the focus of specific paragraphs within the text.

Name _____

WRITTEN RESPONSE TO THE SELECTION

Look Back and Write Look back at pages 68–69. Do all the astronauts do the same job? Provide evidence to support your answer.

Use the list in the box below to help you as you write.

REMEMBER—YOU SHOULD

- [ ] tell whether or not all of the astronauts do the same jobs.

- [ ] use details from the story as well as the photographs to support your answer.

- [ ] be sure you explain your ideas clearly for the reader.

- [ ] try to use correct spelling, capitalization, punctuation, grammar, and sentences.

Common Core State Standards

CCSS Writing 2. Write informative/explanatory texts in which they introduce a topic, use facts and definitions to develop points, and provide a concluding statement or section. (Also **CCSS Informational Text 3., CCSS Language 1., CCSS Language 2., CCSS Language 3.**)

Name _____

VOCABULARY

Directions

Read each sentence. Fill in the circle next to the word that fills the blank.

1 I _____ find my keys anywhere.

- ○ wasn't
- ○ isn't
- ● couldn't

2 Grandma would _____ for us to visit.

- ○ country
- ○ begin
- ● love

3 My dad and I are going to _____ a birdhouse.

- ● build
- ○ hear
- ○ straight

4 Is your _____ coming to see you in the play?

- ○ shoe
- ○ bear
- ● mother

5 My _____ plays the French horn.

- ○ cloud
- ● father
- ○ face

Common Core State Standards

Questions 1–5: **CCSS Foundational Skills 3.f.** Recognize and read grade-appropriate irregularly spelled words.

PHONICS

Directions

Read each sentence and the question that follows. Fill in the circle next to the answer.

6 My uncle drives a **black** car.

Which word has the same sound as **bl** in **black**?

- ○ belt
- ● blink
- ○ ball

7 She's carrying her baby in a **sling**.

Which word has the same sound as **sl** in **sling**?

- ○ soul
- ○ swing
- ● sleep

8 **Skunks** are really stinky!

Which word has the same sound as **sk** in **skunk**?

- ○ kiss
- ○ sake
- ● skate

9 I **lost** my place in my book.

Which word has the same sound as **st** in **lost**?

- ● first
- ○ loss
- ○ salt

10 I like to **camp** out in my backyard.

Which word has the same sound as **mp** in **camp**?

- ○ can't
- ○ came
- ● stomp

GO ON

Common Core State Standards

Questions 6–10: **CCSS Foundational Skills 3.** Know and apply grade-level phonics and word analysis skills in decoding words.

Name _____

COMPREHENSION

The Noisy, Quiet Woods

Tim lived in the city. It was very noisy with all the trucks, cars, and people. He thought about how quiet the woods must be. He wished that he could go there.

One day his mom said, "Let's go camping!" Tim was so excited. He would finally know what quiet sounded like.

They packed some clothes, a tent, and fishing poles. They brought sleeping bags, food, and water. Then Tim and his parents got in the car. They drove for two hours to get to the woods.

It was very quiet. There were no noisy trucks, no cars, and no people. They hiked into the woods. When they came to a river, they stopped. They set up their tent.

Tim's dad showed him how to fish. Together they caught four trout. His mom made a fire. His dad cooked the fish for dinner. They sat by the fire. They looked at the stars. They talked. It got late.

They were very tired. It was time for bed. Tim's mom put out the fire. They all lay down in their sleeping bags. Tim heard an owl hoot. He heard crickets. He heard frogs. Tim could not fall asleep. It was really noisy in the woods!

Directions

Read each question. Fill in the circle next to the best answer.

11 Who is the main character of the story?

- ○ Mom
- ● Tim
- ○ Dad

12 Where do Tim and his parents go?

- ○ to the store
- ○ to the library
- ● to the woods

13 Where did they set up their tent?

- ○ under a tree
- ○ in a cave
- ● next to a river

14 Who cooks fish for dinner?

- ○ Mom
- ● Dad
- ○ Tim

15 What does Tim learn about the woods?

- ● It is noisy there.
- ○ It is a scary place.
- ○ He doesn't like it there.

GO ON

Common Core State Standards

Questions 11–15: CCSS Literature 3. Describe how characters in a story respond to major events and challenges.

Name _____

WRITTEN RESPONSE TO THE SELECTION

Look Back and Write Look back at page 101. What are the Big Dipper and the Little Dipper? Provide evidence to support your answer.

Use the list in the box below to help you as you write.

REMEMBER—YOU SHOULD

☐ explain what the Big Dipper and the Little Dipper are.

☐ use details to help you describe the Big Dipper and Little Dipper for the reader.

☐ use examples from the text to support your answer.

☐ try to use correct spelling, capitalization, punctuation, grammar, and sentences.

GO ON

Common Core State Standards

CCSS Informational Text 3. Describe the connection between a series of historical events, scientific ideas or concepts, or steps in technical procedures in a text. (Also **CCSS Writing 2., CCSS Language 1., CCSS Language 2., CCSS Language 3.**)

Name _____

VOCABULARY

Directions
Read each sentence. Fill in the circle next to the word that fills the blank.

1 The lake is filled with cold _____.
- ○ air
- ○ clouds
- ● water

2 My _____ are light blue.
- ○ arms
- ● eyes
- ○ feet

3 We have to get up _____ to go fishing.
- ● early
- ○ yesterday
- ○ hopefully

4 Many _____ live on her farm.
- ○ rivers
- ● animals
- ○ schools

5 The freezer is _____ of food.
- ○ tired
- ○ warm
- ● full

GO ON

Common Core State Standards

Questions 1–5: CCSS Foundational Skills 3.f. Recognize and read grade-appropriate irregularly spelled words.

PHONICS

Directions

Choose the correct ending for the underlined word. Fill in the circle next to the answer.

6 He likes <u>talk</u> to other people.
- ○ talks
- ● talking
- ○ talked

7 They <u>drop</u> the heavy box.
- ● dropped
- ○ dropping
- ○ droped

8 Geoffrey always <u>play</u> at my house.
- ○ playing
- ○ playys
- ● plays

9 Julianna <u>enjoy</u> going camping last summer.
- ● enjoyed
- ○ enjoys
- ○ enjoying

10 She <u>wipe</u> her hands on the towel.
- ○ wipeed
- ● wiped
- ○ wipped

GO ON

⌐ **Common Core State Standards** ⌐

Questions 6–10: **CCSS Foundational Skills 3.** Know and apply grade-level phonics and word analysis skills in decoding words.

Name _____

COMPREHENSION

Art Is All Over!

It can be big or small. It can be over your head or under your feet. It's art. And it's all over!

Go for a walk in the park. Do you see something that makes you ask, "What's that?" It might be a tree or a flower. Or it might be art!

In some cities, you might not know what you are seeing. A fun idea in New York made a street corner into a baseball field. Home plate was on one corner. People who walked across the street walked through the "field" without knowing it! It was supposed to make people ask, "Was that there yesterday?"

Another great art idea happened at an airport. Big, red ants looked like they were coming out of a hole above people's heads. Some people thought they might scare children. But the airport asked children and their parents about them. Both thought that the big ants were cool!

Many cities have places where all people can see art. Some cities have big pictures. They show people's lives. They are painted on the sides of schools. Other places have them too. People have painted these pictures for a long time.

You can also see art in other countries. In Spain, some park benches are made with little pieces of glass or wood. They help form pictures. The art is pretty, and you can sit on it too!

Australia has a work of art that looks like a tower. When the wind blows a certain way, it sounds like it's humming. But you have to listen carefully. The sound isn't heard very much.

So don't forget to look around for art. It might be outside. It might be a picture or drawing in a book. Or even one that you made yourself. No matter where you see art, it's for all people to enjoy!

GO ON

Directions

Read each question. Fill in the circle next to the best answer.

11 What does the author mostly want you to know about art?

- ○ that it's not important
- ○ that it can be hard to see
- ● that it can be seen everywhere

12 One art idea turned a street corner into a

- ● baseball field.
- ○ airport.
- ○ park bench.

13 One of the questions that art can make you ask is,

- ○ "Do I like art?"
- ● "Was that there yesterday?"
- ○ "How do I make art?"

14 Paragraph 6 tells mainly about

- ● park benches in Spain.
- ○ towers in Australia.
- ○ street corners in New York.

15 The author uses the last paragraph mostly to help the reader

- ○ want to read more stories about art.
- ● remember that everyone can enjoy art.
- ○ create works of art.

GO ON

Common Core State Standards

Questions 11, 14–15: CCSS Informational Text 1. Ask and answer such questions as *who, what, where, when, why,* and *how* to demonstrate understanding of key details in a text. **Questions 12–13: CCSS Informational Text 2.** Identify the main topic of a multiparagraph text as well as the focus of specific paragraphs within the text.

Name _____

WRITTEN RESPONSE TO THE SELECTION

Look Back and Write Look back at page 133. How does a jackrabbit protect itself? Provide evidence to support your answer.

Use the list in the box below to help you as you write.

REMEMBER—YOU SHOULD

☐ tell how a jackrabbit protects itself.

☐ think of specific words that tell your reader exactly what a jack rabbit does.

☐ use details from the text to support your answer.

☐ try to use correct spelling, capitalization, punctuation, grammar, and sentences.

Common Core State Standards

CCSS Writing 2. Write informative/explanatory texts in which they introduce a topic, use facts and definitions to develop points, and provide a concluding statement or section. (Also **CCSS Informational Text 1.**, **CCSS Language 1.**, **CCSS Language 2.**, **CCSS Language 3.**)

Name _____

VOCABULARY

Directions
Read each sentence. Fill in the circle next to the word that fills the blank.

1 We walked to school _____.
- ○ even
- ● together
- ○ close

2 The bottle of juice is _____ cold.
- ○ front
- ○ hungry
- ● very

3 I want to _____ to ride a bike.
- ● learn
- ○ think
- ○ pieces

4 Cats _____ sleep during the day.
- ○ until
- ● often
- ○ gone

5 She's sleepy, even _____ she woke up late today.
- ● though
- ○ near
- ○ white

Common Core State Standards
Questions 1–5: CCSS Foundational Skills 3.f. Recognize and read grade-appropriate irregularly spelled words.

PHONICS

Directions

Choose the correct spelling for the underlined word. Fill in the circle next to the answer.

6 It is time to have <u>luntch</u>.

- ● lunch
- ○ lunsh
- ○ lunth

7 She is wearing a new <u>wach</u>.

- ○ wath
- ○ wash
- ● watch

8 A <u>wthale</u> swims in the ocean.

- ○ wale
- ● whale
- ○ wchale

9 That knife is <u>scharp</u>.

- ○ charp
- ○ stharp
- ● sharp

10 The dogs want us to follow <u>chem</u>.

- ● them
- ○ tchem
- ○ shem

GO ON

Common Core State Standards

Questions 6–10: CCSS Foundational Skills 3. Know and apply grade-level phonics and word analysis skills in decoding words.

Name _____

COMPREHENSION

All About Africa

Africa has many countries. Some countries are very small. Others are very big.

Africa is very large. There are different oceans on each side! Most people live in the south. They live near rivers and the oceans. The north is hot and dry. Not as many people live there.

Some people in live in towns. Others live in cities. Many live on farms. There are many groups of people in Africa. Not every person speaks English. One language people speak in Africa is called *Swahili*. In one country, there are more than ten languages!

A famous river is in Africa. It is called the Nile. People have lived near it for many years. People use its water to help grow food. It goes through many different places. People also use this river to get from place to place.

Directions

Read each question. Fill in the circle next to the best answer.

11 The Nile is a

- ○ country in Africa.
- ● river in Africa.
- ○ state in the United States.

12 In Africa there are many groups of

- ○ food.
- ○ rivers.
- ● people.

13 Where do most people in Africa live?

- ○ near the Nile
- ● in the south
- ○ in the north

14 The north of Africa is

- ● hot and dry.
- ○ warm and wet.
- ○ cold and snowy.

15 Swahili is a type of

- ○ country.
- ● language.
- ○ river.

GO ON

Common Core State Standards

Questions 11–15: CCSS Informational Text 1. Ask and answer such questions as *who, what, where, when, why,* and *how* to demonstrate understanding of key details in a text.

Name _____

WRITTEN RESPONSE TO THE SELECTION

Look Back and Write Look back at how the author wrote the play. Identify the elements of dialogue. Use them to write a short play about Little Red Ant and a new character.

Use the list in the box below to help you as you write.

REMEMBER—YOU SHOULD

☐ use the elements of dialogue to write a short play about Little Red Ant and a new character.

☐ think of a beginning, middle, and end to the story you will tell in the play.

☐ write out the lines that Little Red Ant and the new character say to each other.

☐ try to use correct spelling, capitalization, punctuation, grammar, and sentences.

GO ON

Common Core State Standards

CCSS Writing 3. Write narratives in which they recount a well-elaborated event or short sequence of events, include details to describe actions, thoughts, and feelings, use temporal words to signal event order, and provide a sense of closure. (Also **CCSS Literature 3.**, **CCSS Language 1., CCSS Language 2., CCSS Language 3.**)

Property of
Raugust Library
6070 College Lane
Jamestown, ND 58405

Name _____

VOCABULARY

Directions

Read each sentence. Fill in the circle next to the word that fills the blank.

1 He _____ took us to the zoo.

- ● once
- ○ long
- ○ over

2 I ate dinner with my _____ .

- ○ bark
- ○ sound
- ● family

3 Please _____ that box over there.

- ○ break
- ● pull
- ○ gone

4 Do you want to _____ to music?

- ○ though
- ○ mayor
- ● listen

5 She _____ the dog barking outside.

- ○ grew
- ● heard
- ○ early

┌ **Common Core State Standards** ┐
Questions 1–5: CCSS Foundational Skills 3.f. Recognize and read grade-appropriate irregularly spelled words.

- -

PHONICS

Directions

Read each sentence and the question that follows. Fill in the circle next to the answer.

6 I bought a present <u>for</u> Jill's birthday.

Which word has the same sound as the <u>or</u> in <u>for</u>?

● core
○ our
○ worm

7 James and Lily saw a shooting <u>star</u>.

Which word has the same sound as the <u>ar</u> in <u>star</u>?

○ gate
● part
○ many

8 He <u>tore</u> open the letter.

Which word has the same sound as the <u>ore</u> in <u>tore</u>?

○ soup
● worn
○ tar

9 My mother would like <u>more</u> soup.

Which word has the same sound as the <u>ore</u> in <u>more</u>?

● storm
○ most
○ room

10 We visited a <u>farm</u> on our vacation.

Which word has the same sound as the <u>ar</u> in <u>farm</u>?

○ care
○ pail
● car

GO ON

Common Core State Standards

Questions 6–10: CCSS Foundational Skills 3.e. Identify words with inconsistent but common spelling-sound correspondences.

COMPREHENSION

Helen Keller

When Helen Keller was little, she got sick. She got well again. But she could not see or hear. No one could teach her to speak. She lived in a dark and silent world.

When Helen was almost seven, Annie Sullivan became Helen's teacher. Annie knew how to teach people who could not see. She would spell out words with her fingers into Helen's hand. Annie knew that Helen thought it was only a game. Helen did not yet know that everything had a name.

Helen would throw things and break them. Her parents knew she got mad because her world was dark. Annie would come to help. But Helen often tried to fight her. She was angry. But Annie was strong. She made Helen calm.

One afternoon, Annie held Helen's hand in water. She spelled W-A-T-E-R into Helen's hand. She did it over and over.

Helen felt Annie's finger writing the letters into her hand. "I knew then that W-A-T-E-R meant the wonderful cool something that was flowing over my hand," she wrote. "Everything had a name."

Directions

Read each question. Fill in the circle next to the best answer.

11 As a child, Helen Keller could not speak because

○ she could not see.

● she could not hear.

○ she could not spell.

12 How did Annie Sullivan teach words to Helen?

○ by speaking to her

○ by playing a game with her

● by spelling out words in her hand

13 Helen was mad because

○ she could not spell.

● she could not see.

○ she was not strong.

14 How did Annie teach Helen the meaning of the word "W-A-T-E-R"?

● by holding her hands in water and then spelling the word

○ by spelling the word and then writing it

○ by saying the word and then holding her hands in water

15 What did Annie teach Helen by spelling "W-A-T-E-R"?

○ that Annie was her teacher

○ that spelling was easy

● that everything had a name

GO ON

Common Core State Standards

Questions 11–15: CCSS Informational Text 1. Ask and answer such questions as *who, what, where, when, why,* and *how* to demonstrate understanding of key details in a text.

Name _____

WRITTEN RESPONSE TO THE SELECTION

Look Back and Write Look back at page 194. Why does Jim believe that there is no such thing as a bad dog? Provide evidence to support your answer.

Use the list in the box below to help you as you write.

REMEMBER—YOU SHOULD

☐ tell why Jim believes that there is no such thing as a bad dog.

☐ use details from the story to support your answer.

☐ make sure that each sentence you write helps the reader follow what you are writing.

☐ try to use correct spelling, capitalization, punctuation, grammar, and sentences.

GO ON

Common Core State Standards

CCSS Literature 1. Ask and answer such questions as *who, what, where, when, why,* and *how* to demonstrate understanding of key details in a text. (Also **CCSS Language 1.**, **CCSS Language 2.**)

VOCABULARY

Directions
Read each sentence. Fill in the circle next to the word that fills the blank.

1 The clown made us _____.
- ● laugh
- ○ six
- ○ glass

2 This is the _____ day of the week.
- ○ shout
- ○ either
- ● worst

3 May I have a _____ helping?
- ○ sudden
- ● second
- ○ horse

4 _____ wrong about that.
- ○ Tiger
- ● You're
- ○ Match

5 You may _____ go to the store.
- ○ rock
- ○ great
- ● certainly

Common Core State Standards

Questions 1–5: CCSS Foundational Skills 3.f. Recognize and read grade-appropriate irregularly spelled words.

PHONICS

Directions

Choose the correct way to combine the underlined words to form a contraction. Fill in the circle next to the answer.

6 Pepe <u>does not</u> like ice cream.
- ● doesn't
- ○ does'nt
- ○ don't

7 <u>It is</u> hard to make a choice.
- ○ Its
- ● It's
- ○ Its'

8 I think <u>she will</u> like your present.
- ● she'll
- ○ she'l
- ○ sh'ill

9 <u>I am</u> ready to leave.
- ○ I'am
- ○ Im'
- ● I'm

10 Dave <u>cannot</u> take the dog out tonight.
- ○ cann't
- ● can't
- ○ can'not

Common Core State Standards

Questions 6–10: **CCSS Foundational Skills 3.** Know and apply grade-level phonics and word analysis skills in decoding words.

Name _____

COMPREHENSION

Your New Pet

You are going to welcome home a new kitten next week! There are lots of things to do to get ready for your new pet.

Kittens want to know about everything. They will fish around every part of the house. You have to make sure it's safe. Pick up little things like hairpins and put them away. You don't want your kitten to swallow them.

You need a litter box for your kitten. This is its bathroom. Put the box in a quiet corner. A room that people don't use much is a good place. You can also put the box behind a door. Be ready to scoop out the box at least once a day. Your kitten will also need one dish for food and one bowl for water. Keep its dishes clean.

Kittens like places to be soft and warm. They sleep a lot. You don't have to give them anything fancy. An old, soft blanket will do just fine. You can make a special bed for your kitten. It will probably be just as happy to sleep on your bed or on a stuffed chair or pillow. But it's good for a kitten to have a nest of its very own.

Once your kitten comes home, let it explore. Show it a lot of love. Pick up your kitten often and cuddle it. The more a kitten is held, the happier it will be. It will grow into a friendly cat.

Kittens like to play. Play with your kitten every day. All you need is an old shoelace or a piece of string. Drag it on the floor, and the kitten will chase it and jump on it. You can even train a kitten to play "fetch." Throw a small object like a cotton swab. You can teach your kitten to fetch it every time you throw it. If a kitten plays all the time, it will still love to play when it becomes a cat.

GO ON

Directions

Read each question. Fill in the circle next to the best answer.

11 The author wrote this article

- ● to tell you how to take care of a kitten.
- ○ to entertain you with a story about a kitten.
- ○ to explain to you why you should get a kitten.

12 Why does the author tell you to cuddle your new kitten often?

- ○ so it will play games with you
- ○ so it will catch a lot of mice
- ● so it will become a friendly cat

13 The author warns you to pick up small things and put them away so that

- ○ your house will be neat.
- ● your kitten will be safe.
- ○ you can find them again.

14 What does the author want you to do?

- ○ take your kitten to the vet
- ○ teach your kitten tricks
- ● treat your kitten well

15 How do you think the author feels about kittens?

- ● She likes them.
- ○ She does not like them.
- ○ She has no feelings about them.

GO ON

Common Core State Standards

Questions 11–15: CCSS Informational Text 6. Identify the main purpose of a text, including what the author wants to answer, explain, or describe.

Name _____

WRITTEN RESPONSE TO THE SELECTION

Look Back and Write Look back at 237. Why do you think people call Abraham Lincoln "America's Great President"? Provide evidence to support your answer.

Use the list in the box below to help you as you write.

REMEMBER—YOU SHOULD

☐ explain why people call Abraham Lincoln "America's Great President."

☐ write about what happened when Lincoln was President.

☐ use details from the text to support your answer.

☐ try to use correct spelling, capitalization, punctuation, grammar, and sentences.

GO ON

Common Core State Standards

CCSS Informational Text 1. Ask and answer such questions as *who, what, where, when, why,* and *how* to demonstrate understanding of key details in a text. (Also **CCSS Writing 1., CCSS Writing 2., CCSS Writing 5., CCSS Language 1., CCSS Language 2.**)

Weekly Test 7 Unit 2 Week 2

Name _____

VOCABULARY

Directions
Read each sentence. Fill in the circle next to the word that fills the blank.

1 I ate a _____ apple.

- ○ laugh
- ○ street
- ● whole

2 Walk _____ the bus stop.

- ● toward
- ○ jump
- ○ green

3 The box is on the shelf _____ the stove.

- ● above
- ○ after
- ○ cup

4 I can never remember how to spell that _____ .

- ○ ago
- ● word
- ○ letter

5 Be sure to give the plant _____ water.

- ● enough
- ○ thirsty
- ○ flower

GO ON

Common Core State Standards

Questions 1–5: CCSS Foundational Skills 3.f. Recognize and read grade-appropriate irregularly spelled words.

PHONICS

Directions

Choose the correct way to spell the word that belongs in the blank space. Fill in the circle next to the answer.

6 Our _____ is moving to a new town.

- ○ teachir
- ● teacher
- ○ teachur

7 Bill will be in _____ grade next year.

- ○ thurd
- ● third
- ○ therd

8 The _____ fixed our sink last Friday.

- ○ plumbir
- ○ plumbur
- ● plumber

9 I _____ left at the corner.

- ● turned
- ○ tirned
- ○ terned

10 _____ the soup.

- ○ Ster
- ● Stir
- ○ Stur

Common Core State Standards

Questions 6–10: **CCSS Foundational Skills 3.e.** Identify words with inconsistent but common spelling-sound correspondences.

Name _____

COMPREHENSION

Potatoes

Potatoes are one of the foods we eat. People eat potatoes for lunch and dinner. They also eat them for breakfast. They are not fruits or vegetables. They are the parts of the plant's roots.

It is very easy to grow potatoes in a garden. A potato grows from its "eyes." These are the dark marks on the potato. Have you ever left one in your kitchen for too long? It will start to grow. You will see little green bumps. These bumps will grow into a new potato plant. But the plant will not do well in the kitchen. A potato needs to grow in the ground.

In the past, some people only have had potatoes to eat. One of these places was Ireland in the early 1900s. One year the potato crop did not do well. People had nothing to eat. Many of them came to America at that time. They hoped to find a better life.

The Irish found many ways to cook potatoes. That way no one got tired of eating them. Today, some of our favorite snacks are made from potatoes. Who does not love potato chips and French fries?

Directions

Read each question. Fill in the circle next to the best answer.

11 A potato is

- ○ a fruit.
- ○ a vegetable.
- ● not a fruit or a vegetable.

12 The dark marks that potatoes grow from are called

- ○ roots.
- ● eyes.
- ○ ears.

13 What does a potato need to grow?

- ○ to be left in the kitchen
- ● to be planted in the ground
- ○ to be mashed

14 Where did people have nothing to eat because they could not grow potatoes?

- ● Ireland
- ○ America
- ○ France

15 A food made from potatoes is

- ● French fries.
- ○ vitamins.
- ○ buds.

GO ON

Common Core State Standards

Questions 11–15: CCSS Informational Text 1. Ask and answer such questions as *who, what, where, when, why,* and *how* to demonstrate understanding of key details in a text.

Name _____

WRITTEN RESPONSE TO THE SELECTION

Look Back and Write Look back at pages 260–261. Why isn't the company selling juice? Provide evidence to support your answer.

Use the list in the box below to help you as you write.

REMEMBER—YOU SHOULD

☐ explain why the company isn't selling juice.

☐ use facts from the text to help your reader understand your writing.

☐ be sure each sentence you write helps the reader understand your writing.

☐ try to use correct spelling, capitalization, punctuation, grammar, and sentences.

GO ON

2 Copyright © Pearson Education, Inc., or its affiliates. All Rights Reserved.

Common Core State Standards

CCSS Informational Text 1. Ask and answer such questions as *who, what, where, when, why,* and *how* to demonstrate understanding of key details in a text. (Also **CCSS Writing 2., CCSS Writing 5., CCSS Language 1., CCSS Language 2.**)

Name _____

VOCABULARY

Directions

Read each sentence. Fill in the circle next to the word that fills the blank.

1 There were many _____ at the park.

- ● people
- ○ floors
- ○ pleasant

2 It will _____ rain today.

- ○ step
- ○ fine
- ● probably

3 What _____ we eat for dinner?

- ○ sure
- ● shall
- ○ jump

4 The street name is on the _____.

- ○ tire
- ○ cold
- ● sign

5 Carla _____ a new book.

- ○ scared
- ● bought
- ○ walked

Common Core State Standards

Questions 1–5: CCSS Foundational Skills 3.f. Recognize and read grade-appropriate irregularly spelled words.

PHONICS

Directions

Choose the correct plural form of the underlined word. Fill in the circle next to the answer.

6 **My box has green and white stripes.**

- ○ boxs
- ○ box's
- ● boxes

7 **I packed a lunch for the picnic.**

- ● lunches
- ○ lunchs
- ○ lunchies

8 **The baby giggled and smiled.**

- ○ babys
- ● babies
- ○ babyes

9 **I read a book about pirates.**

- ○ bookes
- ○ book's
- ● books

10 **My favorite flower is the daisy.**

- ○ daisys
- ● daisies
- ○ daisyes

GO ON

Common Core State Standards

Questions 6–10: CCSS Foundational Skills 3.e. Identify words with inconsistent but common spelling-sound correspondences.

Name _____

COMPREHENSION

From Seed to Flower

Most plants begin as seeds. But how does a seed grow into a plant?

It starts when a seed falls to the ground. The seed has a hard shell to protect it. If it is too hot or cold, the seed will not grow. If it is too dry, the seed will not grow. The seed must get wet before it will grow.

When it gets enough water, the seed will start to grow. First, one part of the seed grows into the ground. This part will become the roots. The roots help make the plant strong. The roots also get food and water from the soil.

Another part of the seed grows out of the ground. It grows toward the sun. This part will become the stem and leaves of the plant. The leaves use the light from the sun to help the plant make food.

If the plant gets enough water and sun, it will keep growing. Once it is tall enough, it will stop growing.

Soon flowers will begin to grow on the plant. Flowers are special kinds of leaves. Bugs, such as bees, like flowers and go to them. The bugs help the plants make new seeds. Later, the new seeds will fall to the ground. One of the seeds will start to make a new plant all over again!

Directions

Read each question. Fill in the circle next to the best answer.

11 What must happen before a seed starts to grow?

○ It must make a flower.

○ It must get very cold.

● It must have water.

12 Why do plants have roots?

○ to use light from the sun

● to get food and water from soil

○ to help make new seeds

13 When does a plant stop growing?

○ after it grows flowers

● when it is tall enough

○ after bugs go to it

14 How do leaves help a plant make food?

○ They eat bugs.

○ They fall to the ground.

● They use light from the sun.

15 Which of these helps a plant make new seeds?

● bugs

○ roots

○ leaves

GO ON

Common Core State Standards

Questions 11–15: CCSS Informational Text 3. Describe the connection between a series of historical events, scientific ideas or concepts, or steps in technical procedures in a text.

Name _____

WRITTEN RESPONSE TO THE SELECTION

> **Look Back and Write** Look back at the play. How do you
> know who is speaking? Using the elements of dialogue, write
> a scene about a fifth Bremen Town Musician.

Use the list in the box below to help you as you write.

REMEMBER—YOU SHOULD

☐ write a scene about a fifth Bremen Town Musician.

☐ use the elements of dialogue to write what each character will say
in the scene.

☐ be sure your scene has a beginning, middle, and end.

☐ try to use correct spelling, capitalization, punctuation, grammar,
and sentences.

GO ON

Common Core State Standards

CCSS Literature 6. Acknowledge differences in the points of view of characters, including by speaking in a different voice for each character when reading dialogue aloud. (Also **CCSS Writing 3., CCSS Writing 5., CCSS Language 1., CCSS Language 2.**)

Name _____

VOCABULARY

Directions
Read each sentence. Fill in the circle next to the word that fills the blank.

1 Please close the _____.

- ● door
- ○ hour
- ○ answer

2 _____ got a chance to play.

- ● Everybody
- ○ Chair
- ○ Puzzled

3 Fred _____ the items the teacher asked for.

- ○ promise
- ○ garden
- ● brought

4 I am _____ that I made a mistake.

- ○ valley
- ● sorry
- ○ under

5 The stew will be ready to serve in one _____.

- ○ behind
- ● minute
- ○ question

GO ON

Common Core State Standards

Questions 1–5: CCSS Foundational Skills 3.f. Recognize and read grade-appropriate irregularly spelled words.

PHONICS

Directions

Read each sentence and the question that follows it. Fill in the circle next to the answer.

6 I sent the letter in the <u>rain</u>.

Which word has the same sound as the <u>ai</u> in <u>rain</u>?

- ● paid
- ○ fan
- ○ glad

7 <u>May</u> is my favorite month.

Which word has the same sound as the <u>ay</u> in <u>May</u>?

- ○ lamp
- ○ mad
- ● pain

8 The <u>main</u> building is closed tomorrow.

Which word has the same sound as the <u>ai</u> in <u>main</u>?

- ○ habit
- ● mane
- ○ said

9 Hugo is having a party <u>today</u>.

Which word has the same sound as the <u>ay</u> in <u>today</u>?

- ○ boat
- ● brain
- ○ pan

10 The squirrel hid the <u>acorn</u> carefully.

Which word has the same sound as the <u>a</u> in <u>acorn</u>?

- ○ aunt
- ● stay
- ○ slap

GO ON

Common Core State Standards

Questions 6–10: **CCSS Foundational Skills 3.b.** Know spelling-sound correspondences for additional common vowel teams.

Name _____

COMPREHENSION

The Three Brothers

Once upon a time there were three brothers. The oldest brother was named Andy. The middle brother was named Nick. The youngest brother was called John.

Andy and Nick wanted to make money. They wanted to leave the village and go out into the world. John did not care about becoming rich. But he was friendly, and he went along too.

After seven weeks, the brothers came to a town. They found the people having fun and eating a lot of food. Andy liked to eat. He met Barbara, the girl who had cooked and sold all the food. They became husband and wife, and he stayed in the town.

Nick and John went on their way. After seven weeks, they came to a large city. Nick stepped on something hard in the street. He bent down and picked it up. It was a lump of gold.

"I'm rich!" cried Nick. "I will stay here in the city and buy a fine house to live in."

John was happy that his brothers had found their riches. He walked on. After seven weeks, he arrived back in his own village.

John opened the door of the house. There was the table and the stove. There was his little bed in the corner. *Home is best after all*, John thought. *I have all my riches right here.*

GO ON

Directions

Read each question. Fill in the circle next to the best answer.

11 John is different from his brothers because he

- ● does not care about becoming rich.
- ○ likes to eat.
- ○ leaves home for a long trip.

12 How are Andy and Nick alike?

- ● They both want to be rich.
- ○ They both find gold.
- ○ They both like to eat.

13 All three brothers are alike because

- ○ they all think that home is the best place to be.
- ○ they all want to marry Barbara.
- ● they all leave home on a long trip.

14 Andy and John are different because

- ○ one is nice, and one is mean.
- ● one is youngest, and one is oldest.
- ○ one works hard, and one is lazy.

15 Which event happens to all three brothers?

- ○ Each one marries a beautiful girl.
- ● Each one finds riches.
- ○ Each one wants to find his way home.

GO ON

Common Core State Standards

Questions 11–14: CCSS Literature 3. Describe how characters in a story respond to major events and challenges.
Question 15: CCSS Literature 1. Ask and answer such questions as *who, what, where, when, why,* and *how* to demonstrate understanding of key details in a text.

Name _____

WRITTEN RESPONSE TO THE SELECTION

Look Back and Write Look back at pages 324–325. What does the mouse mean by "one good turn deserves another"? Provide evidence to support your answer.

Use the list in the box below to help you as you write.

REMEMBER—YOU SHOULD

☐ explain what the mouse means by "one good turn deserves another."

☐ use words such as *first*, *next*, and *then* to tell what happened in the correct order.

☐ use details from the story to support your writing.

☐ try to use correct spelling, capitalization, punctuation, grammar, and sentences.

GO ON

Common Core State Standards

CCSS Literature 2. Recount stories, including fables and folktales from diverse cultures, and determine their central message, lesson, or moral. (Also **CCSS Writing 5., CCSS Language 1., CCSS Language 2.**)

Name _____

VOCABULARY

Directions

Read each sentence. Fill in the circle next to the word that fills the blank.

1 I like _____ class best.
- ○ apple
- ● science
- ○ leg

2 I can't find my other _____.
- ● shoe
- ○ grass
- ○ snow

3 Mia _____ the game.
- ○ gold
- ○ sings
- ● won

4 Can you _____ how old I am?
- ● guess
- ○ move
- ○ watch

5 Dan lives in a small _____.
- ○ letter
- ● village
- ○ pretty

GO ON

Common Core State Standards

Questions 1–5: CCSS Foundational Skills 3.f. Recognize and read grade-appropriate irregularly spelled words.

PHONICS

Directions
Read each sentence and the question that follows it. Fill in the circle next to the answer.

6 We studied <u>leaves</u> in science class.

Which word has the same sound as the ea in <u>leaves</u>?

- ○ senses
- ● flee
- ○ live

7 The teacher was <u>happy</u> at the end of the week.

Which word has the same sound as the y in <u>happy</u>?

- ● meter
- ○ hopeful
- ○ glad

8 The ocean is very <u>deep</u>.

Which word has the same sound as the ee in <u>deep</u>?

- ○ blue
- ● pony
- ○ rough

9 I got a <u>seat</u> in the front row.

Which word has the same sound as the ea in <u>seat</u>?

- ○ toes
- ○ set
- ● cheese

10 John walked home with <u>me</u>.

Which word has the same sound as the e in <u>me</u>?

- ○ Jane
- ○ Helen
- ● Steve

GO ON

Common Core State Standards

Questions 6–10: CCSS Foundational Skills 3.b. Know spelling-sound correspondences for additional common vowel teams.

Name _____

COMPREHENSION

Ducks

Ducks are a kind of small bird. People often see ducks in places with water, such as ponds or streams. But they can live on water or on land.

There are many different kinds of ducks. All ducks have webbed feet that they use for swimming. Their feet help them paddle in the water. When a duck walks, it moves from side to side because of its feet. A duck's feet also help keep it warm. When a duck swims in very cold water, it does not feel the cold in its feet.

Another way that a duck stays warm is its feathers. Duck feathers are fluffy and soft. A duck likes to keep its feathers clean. It does this by moving its nose, or "beak," through its feathers. This is called "preening." Ducks clean themselves very often.

A duck's mouth is called a "bill." A duck uses its bill to hold food. A duck's bill can be long or short. Some ducks use their bills to find bugs and seeds in the mud. Other ducks use them to go under the water to catch fish. But most ducks use their bill to make a special sound called a "quack." This funny sound can be very loud. It is a duck's way of talking to other ducks, and to people!

Directions
Read each question. Fill in the circle next to the best answer.

11 The author wrote this article

- ● to tell you all about ducks.
- ○ to get you to help ducks.
- ○ so you can enjoy stories about water.

12 The author includes information about a duck's beak in paragraph 3

- ○ to get people to like ducks.
- ○ to explain how ducks keep warm in the water.
- ● to explain how ducks clean themselves.

13 The author wrote paragraph 4 to

- ○ show you how a duck finds food.
- ○ tell you how a duck cleans itself.
- ● explain how a duck uses its bill.

14 What does the author want you to do?

- ○ Understand how ducks talk to each other.
- ● Think about ducks whenever you see them.
- ○ Compare a duck's beak with its bill.

15 How does the author feel about a duck's "quack"?

- ● He thinks it is not like other sounds.
- ○ He wishes the sound were louder.
- ○ He has no feelings about it.

GO ON

┌ **Common Core State Standards**

Questions 11–15: CCSS Informational Text 6. Identify the main purpose of a text, including what the author wants to answer, explain, or describe.

WRITTEN RESPONSE TO THE SELECTION

Look Back and Write Look back at page 369. Why do you think the talking robot didn't win a prize? Provide evidence to support your answer.

Use the list in the box below to help you as you write.

REMEMBER—YOU SHOULD

☐ tell why you think the talking robot didn't win a prize.

☐ use details from the story to support your answer.

☐ make sure the reasons you tell about are clear to the reader.

☐ try to use correct spelling, capitalization, punctuation, grammar, and sentences.

GO ON

┌ **Common Core State Standards** ┐

CCSS Writing 3. Write narratives in which they recount a well-elaborated event or short sequence of events, include details to describe actions, thoughts, and feelings, use temporal words to signal event order, and provide a sense of closure. (Also **CCSS Language 1.**)

Name _____

VOCABULARY

Directions

Read each sentence. Fill in the circle next to the word that fills the blank.

1 My mom has a _____ of me.

○ chair
● picture
○ nose

2 What time do you go to _____?

○ ant
○ kite
● school

3 Marcus gave the right _____.

○ company
○ hill
● answer

4 Are your _____ home?

○ wash
● parents
○ songs

5 She will visit a _____ place.

● faraway
○ best
○ hold

GO ON

Common Core State Standards

Questions 1–5: CCSS Foundational Skills 3.f. Recognize and read grade-appropriate irregularly spelled words.

PHONICS

Directions

Read each sentence and the question that follows it. Fill in the circle next to the answer.

6 At the market the cherries were already <u>sold</u>.

Which word has the same sound as the <u>o</u> in <u>sold</u>?

- ● boat
- ○ gone
- ○ top

7 Sarah read the <u>joke</u> to the class.

Which word has the same sound as the <u>o</u> in <u>joke</u>?

- ○ town
- ● know
- ○ lesson

8 Manny found a <u>toad</u> on his way to school.

Which word has the same sound as the <u>oa</u> in <u>toad</u>?

- ○ mouse
- ● bowl
- ○ owl

9 Giles rode on the <u>slowest</u> train car.

Which word has the same sound as the <u>ow</u> in <u>slowest</u>?

- ○ longest
- ● oldest
- ○ loudest

10 The toy was <u>broken</u>.

Which word has the same sound as the <u>o</u> in <u>broken</u>?

- ○ good
- ○ lost
- ● close

GO ON

Common Core State Standards

Questions 6–10: CCSS Foundational Skills 3.b. Know spelling-sound correspondences for additional common vowel teams.

COMPREHENSION

The Surprise

Lars's father was having a hard time at work. Lars had a plan to cheer him up. Today was his dad's birthday.

Lars went to the store after school. At home, he asked his mom for permission and then started working. Using a cookbook, he mixed eggs, butter, sugar, and chocolate together. He poured the mix into a pan, and his mom put it in the oven.

The house filled with the smell of cake. It was almost ready!

When Lars's father came home from work, he looked tired. Then he smelled the cake and smiled.

Lars called his mother and sister into the kitchen. They all sat at the table and sang "Happy Birthday." Then Lars's mom took the cake out of the oven and put it in the middle of the table.

But the cake did not look right. It was lumpy and filled with air bubbles. It was brown on the sides and yellow in the middle. It was hard on top and soft on the bottom. Lars ran out of the room.

His father went to find him in his bedroom. "Lars, it was very nice of you to make me a cake," he said.

"The cake is a mess!" Lars said.

"No, it isn't," his father said. "Just because something doesn't look good doesn't mean it doesn't taste good. Your cake is the best birthday cake I've ever had."

Lars and his father went back to the kitchen. Lars ate a large slice. His frown turned into a smile. "It does taste great!"

GO ON

Directions

Read each question. Fill in the circle next to the best answer.

11 Why does Lars go to the store?

○ to buy his dad a gift

● to buy things to make a cake

○ to see his father

12 Why does Lars make the cake?

○ His mother is having a birthday.

○ He wants to bring it to school.

● He wants to make his dad feel better.

13 How does Lars learn to make the cake?

● He reads the directions.

○ His mother shows him.

○ He asks his teacher.

14 Why does Lars run out of the kitchen?

● because he feels bad about the cake

○ to play hide-and-seek

○ to get his dad's birthday gift

15 What does Lars learn from his father?

○ The cake is a mess.

● The cake looks bad but tastes good.

○ The family will go out for dinner.

GO ON

2 Copyright © Pearson Education, Inc., or its affiliates. All Rights Reserved.

Common Core State Standards

Questions 11–15: CCSS Literature 3. Describe how characters in a story respond to major events and challenges.

Name _____

WRITTEN RESPONSE TO THE SELECTION

Look Back and Write Look back at page 391. How does Juno know who sent the letter? Provide evidence to support your answer.

Use the list in the box below to help you as you write.

REMEMBER—YOU SHOULD

☐ tell how Juno knows who sent the letter.

☐ include at least three clues from the story in your writing.

☐ make sure you include all the important information that helps to answer the question.

☐ try to use correct spelling, capitalization, punctuation, grammar, and sentences.

GO ON

Common Core State Standards

CCSS Writing 3. Write narratives in which they recount a well-elaborated event or short sequence of events, include details to describe actions, thoughts, and feelings, use temporal words to signal event order, and provide a sense of closure. (Also **CCSS Literature 3.**, **CCSS Language 1.**)

Name _____

VOCABULARY

Directions
Read each sentence. Fill in the circle next to the word that fills the blank.

1 It is going to snow _____.
- ○ gone
- ○ our
- ● tomorrow

2 I will do _____ I can to help.
- ○ begin
- ○ close
- ● whatever

3 She _____ a fish at the lake.
- ● caught
- ○ drove
- ○ laughed

4 I don't _____ that story!
- ○ when
- ● believe
- ○ finally

5 Pablo has _____ playing all day.
- ● been
- ○ could
- ○ today

GO ON

Common Core State Standards

Questions 1–5: CCSS Foundational Skills 3.f. Recognize and read grade-appropriate irregularly spelled words.

WORD ANALYSIS

Directions

Read each question. Fill in the circle next to the answer.

6   <u>Greenhouse</u> is a compound word.

You can tell from the two parts of the word that a <u>greenhouse</u> is

○ a place where candy is made.

○ a place that is new.

● a place where plants grow.

7   <u>Clockwork</u> is a compound word.

You can tell from the two parts of the word that, when something is like <u>clockwork</u>, it is

● on time.

○ moving in a line.

○ happening in the morning.

8   <u>Mailbox</u> is a compound word.

You can tell from the two parts of the word that a <u>mailbox</u> is

○ a bag to carry books.

● a place to put letters.

○ a book that holds stamps.

9   <u>Cookbook</u> is a compound word.

You can tell from the two parts of the word that a <u>cookbook</u> lists

○ the meanings of words.

○ math problems.

● directions for making food.

10   <u>Bedtime</u> is a compound word.

You can tell from the two parts of the word that <u>bedtime</u> is

○ the hour for making your bed.

● the hour for going to sleep.

○ the hour for eating breakfast.

GO ON

2 Copyright © Pearson Education, Inc., or its affiliates. All Rights Reserved.

Common Core State Standards

Questions 6–10: CCSS Language 4.d. Use knowledge of the meaning of individual words to predict the meaning of compound words (e.g., *birdhouse, lighthouse, housefly; bookshelf, notebook, bookmark*).

Name _____

COMPREHENSION

The Sunset

Sol and Luna were good friends who lived in the sky. They had important jobs. During the day, Sol held up the sun. During the night, Luna held up the moon.

But Sol and Luna were unhappy. They loved their jobs, and they were glad to help the people on Earth. The problem was that Sol and Luna were always working.

While Sol worked, Luna painted beautiful pictures for their house. While Luna worked, Sol cooked food for them to eat. But they never got to enjoy them together.

So they continued their work for many years until one day when Luna, in a rush to get to work, kicked over her jars of paint.

Suddenly, the night sky was filled with orange, purple, yellow, and gray. In his surprise, Sol put down the sun. They stood side by side, watching the beautiful colors.

From that day on, they had time to spend together. Each night, Luna spilled her paints. Then Sol and Luna ate dinner and talked until it was time for Luna to hold up the moon.

Directions

Read each question. Fill in the circle next to the best answer.

11 How is Sol's job and Luna's job alike?

- ○ They both work on Earth.
- ● They both hold up objects in the sky.
- ○ They both cook meals and paint pictures.

12 How is Sol's job different from Luna's job?

- ○ Sol holds up the moon, and Luna holds up the sun.
- ○ Sol holds up the sun, and Luna holds up the night sky.
- ● Sol holds up the sun, and Luna holds up the moon.

13 What problem did Sol and Luna both have?

- ● They did not get to spend time together.
- ○ They did not like their jobs.
- ○ They did not like to work hard.

14 How is the sky different after Luna's paints spill?

- ● It is filled with many colors.
- ○ It gets very dark.
- ○ It is stormy and gray.

15 How is the friendship between Luna and Sol different after Luna's paints spill?

- ○ They do not have to work ever again.
- ● They get to spend time together every day.
- ○ They stop eating dinner.

GO ON

Common Core State Standards

Questions 11–12, 14: CCSS Literature 1. Ask and answer such questions as *who, what, where, when, why,* and *how* to demonstrate understanding of key details in a text. **Questions 13, 15: CCSS Literature 3.** Describe how characters in a story respond to major events and challenges.

Name _____

WRITTEN RESPONSE TO THE SELECTION

Look Back and Write Look back at page 435. Why does Anansi not feel full? Provide evidence to support your answer.

Use the list in the box below to help you as you write.

REMEMBER—YOU SHOULD

☐ tell why Anasi does not feel full.

☐ use descriptive words that tell how Anansi feels.

☐ use neat handwriting so that the reader can understand what you are writing.

☐ try to use correct spelling, capitalization, punctuation, grammar, and sentences.

GO ON

Common Core State Standards

CCSS Writing 3. Write narratives in which they recount a well-elaborated event or short sequence of events, include details to describe actions, thoughts, and feelings, use temporal words to signal event order, and provide a sense of closure. (Also **CCSS Literature 3.**, **CCSS Language 1.**)

Name _____

VOCABULARY

Directions

Read each sentence. Fill in the circle next to the word that fills the blank.

1 _____ car is new.

- ○ Late
- ● Their
- ○ When

2 There are _____ books on the desk.

- ○ front
- ● many
- ○ round

3 I need to _____ some milk.

- ● buy
- ○ listen
- ○ care

4 He has three _____.

- ○ grass
- ○ water
- ● daughters

5 Julie is my _____ sister.

- ● youngest
- ○ alone
- ○ together

Common Core State Standards

Questions 1–5: CCSS Foundational Skills 3.f. Recognize and read grade-appropriate irregularly spelled words.

PHONICS

Directions

Read each sentence. Fill in the circle of the word with the long *i* sound that fills the blank.

6 The _____ are on the plane.

- ○ wings
- ○ girls
- ● pilots

7 Can that baby bird _____ now?

- ○ chirp
- ● fly
- ○ sing

8 Please help me _____ my penny.

- ● find
- ○ give
- ○ toss

9 The sun is so _____ today.

- ○ big
- ● bright
- ○ smooth

10 Help that little _____ climb those steps.

- ● child
- ○ kitten
- ○ girl

GO ON

Common Core State Standards

Questions 6–10: CCSS Foundational Skills 3.a. Distinguish long and short vowels when reading regularly spelled one-syllable words.

Name _____

COMPREHENSION

Moms Can Learn Too

Mom came through the back door and slammed it.

"Mom, why are you shaking?" said Mark. "What's wrong?"

"I thought I saw a piece of black rubber in my flower bed. When I tried to pick it up, it moved! It was a snake!"

"But Mom," said Dina. "That's a black snake. It will not hurt you. We read about black snakes in science class."

Mom sat down. After a moment, she said, "I am going to get over my fear of snakes. And you two are going to help me."

Mom, Mark, and Dina went to the library. They searched on the Web. They found everything they could about snakes. Mom said, "The more you know about something, the less you are afraid of it."

Then Mom said, "Here are pictures of the poisonous snakes in our state. They could bite you and make you very sick. We should stay far away from these snakes."

Mark said, "Mom, are you going to make friends with snakes now?"

"I won't go that far," said Mom. "But now I will not be so afraid."

Directions

Read each question. Fill in the circle next to the best answer.

11 Which of these happens first?

- ○ Mom goes to the library with Mark and Dina.
- ○ Mom shows Mark and Dina pictures of poisonous snakes.
- ● Mom sees a snake in the flower bed.

12 What happens right after Mom sees a snake?

- ● She starts shaking.
- ○ She decides to get over her fear of snakes.
- ○ She goes to the library with Mark and Dina.

13 What happens right after Mom decides to get over her fear of snakes?

- ○ She does a Web search on snakes.
- ● She goes to the library with Mark and Dina.
- ○ She shows Mark and Dina pictures of poisonous snakes.

14 What is the first thing Mom, Mark, and Dina do at the library?

- ○ They look at pictures of poisonous snakes.
- ○ They find everything they can about snakes.
- ● They search the Web.

15 Which of these happens last?

- ○ Mom shows Mark and Dina pictures of poisonous snakes.
- ● Mom decides to be less afraid of snakes.
- ○ Mark and Dina read about snakes in science class.

GO ON

Common Core State Standards

Questions 11–15: CCSS Literature 5. Describe the overall structure of a story, including describing how the beginning introduces the story and the ending concludes the action.

Name _____

WRITTEN RESPONSE TO THE SELECTION

Look Back and Write Look back at page 462. How are the sisters alike and different? Provide evidence to support your answer.

Use the list in the box below to help you as you write.

REMEMBER — YOU SHOULD

☐   tell how the sisters are alike and different.

☐   be sure each sentence tells about Rosa or Blanca.

☐   use details from the story to support your answer.

☐   try to use correct spelling, capitalization, punctuation, grammar, and sentences.

GO ON

Common Core State Standards

CCSS Literature 3. Describe how characters in a story respond to major events and challenges. (Also **CCSS Writing 3.**, **CCSS Writing 5.**)

Name _____

VOCABULARY

Directions
Read each sentence. Fill in the circle next to the word that fills the blank.

1 There is _____ one cookie left.
- ○ some
- ○ everything
- ● only

2 That is a good _____.
- ○ words
- ● question
- ○ their

3 David wants to buy some new _____.
- ● clothes
- ○ taught
- ○ caves

4 Sam makes _____ by raking leaves.
- ○ pens
- ○ hours
- ● money

5 My _____ has two dogs.
- ● neighbor
- ○ every
- ○ ear

GO ON

Common Core State Standards

Questions 1–5: CCSS Foundational Skills 3.f. Recognize and read grade-appropriate irregularly spelled words.

WORD ANALYSIS

Directions
Read each question. Fill in the circle next to the answer.

6 What is the correct way to write "more happy"?

- ○ happyer
- ● happier
- ○ happiest

7 What is the correct way to write "most hot"?

- ○ hotest
- ○ hoter
- ● hottest

8 What is the correct way to write "most angry"?

- ● angriest
- ○ angryest
- ○ angrier

9 In which sentence is the underlined word NOT used correctly?

- ○ The sky is <u>bluest</u> in August.
- ○ His garden is <u>drier</u> than mine.
- ● Tim's lawn is <u>greenest</u> than Rose's.

10 In which sentence is the underlined word NOT used correctly?

- ○ The music was <u>louder</u> yesterday.
- ○ He will be on stage <u>sooner</u> than you think.
- ● Tomorrow will be the <u>busier</u> day of all.

GO ON

Common Core State Standards

Questions 6–10: CCSS Foundational Skills 3.d. Decode words with common prefixes and suffixes.

Name _____

COMPREHENSION

Amelia Earhart

Amelia Earhart is more famous than any other woman. She was the first woman to fly across the ocean. She won many prizes for her flying.

Amelia Earhart was born in 1897. In 1920 she went up in an airplane for the first time. She took a ten-minute trip over Los Angeles. The ride changed her life. She was so excited that she decided to become a pilot. She saved up her money and bought her own airplane.

At the time, cars were a new invention. Very few people had ever been in a plane. Many people said that flying airplanes was not a job for women. But Amelia did not listen. She did not want to stay home. She wanted to fly.

Amelia Earhart flew across the Atlantic Ocean and then the Pacific Ocean. She knew that flying was dangerous, but she was not afraid.

In 1937 she set out to be the first woman to fly around the world alone. However, she and her plane went missing over the Pacific Ocean. There will never be another pilot like Amelia Earhart!

GO ON

Directions

Read each question. Fill in the circle next to the best answer.

11 Amelia Earhart was the first woman to fly across

- ● the ocean.
- ○ the sky.
- ○ Los Angeles.

12 The author's statement that Amelia Earhart is more famous than other women is a/an

- ○ fact.
- ● opinion.
- ○ detail.

13 When was Amelia Earhart born?

- ● 1897
- ○ 1920
- ○ 1937

14 Which ocean did Amelia Earhart fly across first?

- ○ The Pacific Ocean
- ● The Atlantic Ocean
- ○ She did not fly across the ocean.

15 The author's statement that there will never be another pilot like Amelia Earhart is a/an

- ○ detail.
- ○ fact.
- ● opinion.

GO ON

Common Core State Standards

Questions 11, 13–14: CCSS Informational Text 1. Ask and answer such questions as *who, what, where, when, why,* and *how* to demonstrate understanding of key details in a text. **Questions 12, 15: CCSS Informational Text 6.** Identify the main purpose of a text, including what the author wants to answer, explain, or describe.

Name _____

WRITTEN RESPONSE TO THE SELECTION

Look Back and Write Look back at page 505. What did George Washington Carver think about money? Provide evidence to support your answer.

Use the list in the box below to help you as you write.

REMEMBER—YOU SHOULD

☐   explain what George Washington Carver thought about money.

☐   use details from the text to support your answer.

☐   reread what you have written to make sure the reader understands what you are saying.

☐   try to use correct spelling, capitalization, punctuation, grammar, and sentences.

GO ON

Common Core State Standards

CCSS Informational Text 1. Ask and answer such questions as *who, what, where, when, why,* and *how* to demonstrate understanding of key details in a text. (Also **CCSS Writing 5., CCSS Language 1.**)

Name _____

VOCABULARY

Directions
Read each sentence. Fill in the circle next to the word that fills the blank.

1 We walked to a _____ in the woods.

- ○ water
- ● clearing
- ○ trees

2 Beth got a _____ score on the test.

- ● perfect
- ○ right
- ○ friendly

3 We _____ to the beach.

- ○ driving
- ○ crashed
- ● traveled

4 Lucy likes _____ in the water.

- ● splashing
- ○ spilling
- ○ drinking

5 Dad went fishing at the _____.

- ○ rain
- ○ moon
- ● pond

GO ON

> **Common Core State Standards**

Questions 1–5: CCSS Language 4. Determine or clarify the meaning of unknown and multiple-meaning words and phrases based on *grade 2 reading and content,* choosing flexibly from an array of strategies.

PHONICS

Directions

Choose the correct way to divide the underlined word into syllables. Fill in the circle next to the answer.

6 My <u>uncle</u> is visiting for the holiday.

- ○ u | ncle
- ● un | cle
- ○ unc | le

7 The <u>battle</u> was fought in 1812.

- ○ batt | le
- ● bat | tle
- ○ ba | ttle

8 Maya plays the <u>bugle</u> in band.

- ○ b | ugle
- ○ bugl | e
- ● bu | gle

9 I have a <u>bundle</u> of wood for our campfire.

- ● bun | dle
- ○ bu | ndle
- ○ bund | le

10 Would you put this bowl on the <u>table</u>, please?

- ○ tab | le
- ○ tabl | e
- ● ta | ble

GO ON

Common Core State Standards

Questions 6–10: CCSS Foundational Skills 3. Know and apply grade-level phonics and word analysis skills in decoding words.

Weekly Test 16 Unit 4 Week 1

Directions

Read each question. Fill in the circle next to the best answer.

11 **Why did Dan visit Nan on the farm?**

- ● His parents wanted him to get away from the summer heat.
- ○ His parents wanted him to work harder.
- ○ Nan wanted him to visit.

12 **Why did Nan wake up before Dan?**

- ○ Dan stayed up late.
- ○ Nan could not sleep.
- ● Nan was used to getting up early.

13 **How does Dan feel about the animals on the farm?**

- ○ He does not like them.
- ● He likes them.
- ○ He has no feelings about them.

14 **Dan is tired every night at first on the farm because**

- ○ he stays up late.
- ○ he cannot sleep.
- ● he has worked hard.

15 **Dan thought his mother would be surprised when he got home because**

- ● he liked getting up early.
- ○ he did not like the farm.
- ○ he did not like Nan.

GO ON

Common Core State Standards

Questions 11–15: CCSS Literature 1. Ask and answer such questions as *who, what, where, when, why,* and *how* to demonstrate understanding of key details in a text.

Name _____

WRITTEN RESPONSE TO THE SELECTION

Look Back and Write Look back at page 34. How does the caterpillar feel about changes? Use details from the selection as you write your answer.

Use the list in the box below to help you as you write.

REMEMBER—YOU SHOULD

☐ tell how the caterpillar feels about changes.

☐ explain why you think the caterpillar feels the way he does.

☐ use details from the story to support your answer.

☐ try to use correct spelling, capitalization, punctuation, grammar, and sentences.

GO ON

Common Core State Standards

CCSS Literature 3. Describe how characters in a story respond to major events and challenges. (Also **CCSS Language 1.**, **CCSS Language 2.**, **CCSS Language 3.**)

Name _____

VOCABULARY

Directions

Read each sentence. Fill in the circle next to the word that fills the blank.

1 I ate some _____ at lunch.
- ● fruit
- ○ play
- ○ green

2 Does this plant need more _____?
- ○ fall
- ● soil
- ○ only

3 This road is very _____.
- ○ music
- ○ around
- ● bumpy

4 It's time to _____ the apples.
- ○ fresh
- ○ smooth
- ● harvest

5 We have a _____ in the garden.
- ○ seven
- ● vine
- ○ front

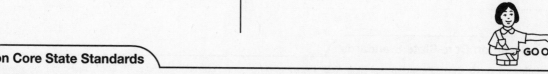

Common Core State Standards

Questions 1–5: **CCSS Language 4.a.** Use sentence-level context as a clue to the meaning of a word or phrase.

PHONICS

Directions

Read each sentence and the question that follows it. Fill in the circle next to the answer.

6 Carmen <u>shook</u> the bottle .

Which word has the same <u>oo</u> sound as in <u>shook</u>?

- ● foot
- ○ proof
- ○ fool

7 Jackie planted a <u>bush</u> in his yard.

Which word has the same <u>u</u> sound as in <u>bush</u>?

- ○ door
- ○ brush
- ● crook

8 This is my favorite <u>book</u>.

Which word has the same <u>oo</u> sound as in <u>book</u>?

- ○ food
- ● put
- ○ shut

9 My bag is <u>full</u> of leaves and sticks.

Which word has the same <u>u</u> sound as in <u>full</u>?

- ● look
- ○ snoop
- ○ nut

10 That squirrel <u>took</u> my peanuts!

Which word has the same <u>oo</u> sound as in <u>took</u>?

- ○ mood
- ○ fun
- ● bull

GO ON

Common Core State Standards

Questions 6, 8, 10: CCSS Foundational Skills 3.b. Know spelling-sound correspondences for additional common vowel teams.
Questions 7, 9: CCSS Foundational Skills 3. Know and apply grade-level phonics and word analysis skills in decoding words.

Name _____

COMPREHENSION

A Great Day

I woke right up this morning.

I was up before the sun.

The adventure we were planning would be filled with lots of fun.

We left our house real early.

All of us were in the car.

Driving over to the fairgrounds, it was really not too far.

It was filled with great big baskets, each with ropes hung all around.

Big, huge sheets of many colors lay all over on the ground.

Then hot air balloons were floating.

They rose up into the sky.

Giant, yellow flames were shooting.

They were reaching way up high.

There were blue and green and brown ones.

There were some with big, red stars.

There were shapes like dogs and kittens, and some frogs and balls and cars.

As I watched them flying higher, they slipped silently away.

I hugged my dad and told him, "Let's see that again, OK?"

Directions

Read each question. Fill in the circle next to the best answer.

11 The narrator in the poem woke

- ○ to get a glass of water.
- ○ after hearing a loud sound.
- ● before sunrise.

12 What time of day did they leave their home?

- ● morning
- ○ noon
- ○ afternoon

13 Where did they go to see the hot air balloons?

- ○ a field
- ○ downtown
- ● the fairgrounds

14 What happened as the narrator watched the hot air balloons?

- ○ Big sheets lay on the ground.
- ○ The shapes turned into dogs and kittens.
- ● The hot air balloons slipped away.

15 What was the last thing that happened in the poem?

- ● The narrator's father got a hug.
- ○ The balloons flew higher.
- ○ The narrator and father went home.

GO ON

Common Core State Standards

Questions 11–13: CCSS Literature 1. Ask and answer such questions as *who, what, where, when, why,* and *how* to demonstrate understanding of key details in a text. **Questions 14–15: CCSS Literature 5.** Describe the overall structure of a story, including describing how the beginning introduces the story and the ending concludes the action.

Weekly Test 17 Unit 4 Week 2

Name _____

WRITTEN RESPONSE TO THE SELECTION

Look Back and Write Look back at page 69. How do bees help pumpkin plants? Provide evidence to support your answer.

Use the list in the box below to help you as you write.

REMEMBER—YOU SHOULD

☐   tell how bees help pumpkin plants.

☐   use words such as *first*, *next*, and *then* to tell what happens in the order it happens.

☐   use details from the text to support your answer.

☐   try to use correct spelling, capitalization, punctuation, grammar, and sentences.

Common Core State Standards

CCSS Writing 2. Write informative/explanatory texts in which they introduce a topic, use facts and definitions to develop points, and provide a concluding statement or section. (Also **CCSS Informational Text 1.**, **CCSS Informational Text 3.**, **CCSS Language 1.**, **CCSS Language 2.**, **CCSS Language 3.**)

Name _____

VOCABULARY

Directions
Read each sentence. Fill in the circle next to the word that fills the blank.

1 There are more stars in the sky than _____ of sand on the beach.

- ○ meats
- ● grains
- ○ break

2 My shirt is made from very thick _____.

- ● material
- ○ water
- ○ glass

3 Tiny _____ make up most things.

- ○ toys
- ○ cabbages
- ● particles

4 Water will _____ into the basement if we don't fix the crack.

- ○ substances
- ● seep
- ○ dissolve

5 The _____ of this blanket feels very soft.

- ○ sound
- ○ measurements
- ● texture

GO ON

Common Core State Standards

Questions 1–5: CCSS Language 4.a. Use sentence-level context as a clue to the meaning of a word or phrase.

PHONICS

Directions

Choose the correct spelling for the underlined word. Fill the circle next to the answer.

6 He <u>foun</u> a quarter on the floor.
- ○ frowned
- ● found
- ○ fown

7 It is time to lie <u>dowed</u>.
- ● down
- ○ downed
- ○ doun

8 The President has a lot of <u>pouwer</u>.
- ○ pouer
- ○ pouder
- ● power

9 Her <u>howse</u> is very big.
- ○ howtse
- ○ hause
- ● house

10 They bought a <u>powned</u> of hamburger meat at the supermarket.
- ● pound
- ○ pownd
- ○ paund

GO ON

Common Core State Standards

Questions 6–10: CCSS Foundational Skills 3.b. Know spelling-sound correspondences for additional common vowel teams.

Name _____

COMPREHENSION

Getting to Know Europe

Europe is about the same size as the United States. But it has more than twice as many people! It is made up of 42 countries. Some of them have more people than any U.S. state.

Part of Europe almost reaches the North Pole. In the south, the weather is very warm, and the sun shines a lot. Italy is in the south. It is the most beautiful country in Europe! It has rolling hills and valleys. Foods such as olives and grapes grow there.

Europe also has many different kinds of people. Their ideas in art and science have spread around the world. There are many factories and farms. People have many choices for places to live and work.

London is the nicest city in Europe. It is the capital of the United Kingdom. The United Kingdom is one of the biggest countries in Europe. London sits on both sides of a famous river. It has many nice streets and neighborhoods. It is known for its art.

GO ON

Directions

Read each question. Fill in the circle next to the best answer.

11 How many countries are in Europe?

- ○ 24
- ● 42
- ○ 50

12 Italy is located in

- ● the south of Europe.
- ○ the north of Europe.
- ○ the United Kingdom.

13 The author's statement that Italy is the most beautiful country in Europe is a/an

- ○ fact.
- ○ detail.
- ● opinion.

14 One of the biggest countries in Europe is

- ○ London.
- ○ Italy.
- ● the United Kingdom.

15 The author states an opinion that the place that has many nice streets and neighborhoods is

- ○ Italy.
- ● London.
- ○ the United Kingdom.

GO ON

Common Core State Standards

Questions 11, 12, 14: CCSS Informational Text 1. Ask and answer such questions as *who, what, where, when, why,* and *how* to demonstrate understanding of key details in a text. **Questions 13, 15: CCSS Informational Text 6.** Identify the main purpose of a text, including what the author wants to answer, explain, or describe.

Name _____

WRITTEN RESPONSE TO THE SELECTION

> **Look Back and Write** Look back at page 95. What is in soil? Provide evidence to support your answer.

Use the list in the box below to help you as you write.

REMEMBER—YOU SHOULD

- [ ] explain what is in soil.

- [ ] use facts from the passage to support your answer.

- [ ] make sure that each sentence you write helps the reader understand what you are saying.

- [ ] try to use correct spelling, capitalization, punctuation, grammar, and sentences.

Common Core State Standards

CCSS Writing 2. Write informative/explanatory texts in which they introduce a topic, use facts and definitions to develop points, and provide a concluding statement or section. (Also **CCSS Informational Text 1., CCSS Informational Text 3., CCSS Language 1., CCSS Language 2., CCSS Language 3.**)

Name _____

VOCABULARY

Directions
Read each sentence. Fill in the circle next to the word that fills the blank.

1 Don't lose your _____ or you will fall.

- ● balance
- ○ rope
- ○ problems

2 My head hurts, so speak in a _____.

- ○ quietly
- ○ bathtub
- ● whisper

3 The strong wind made us _____.

- ● sway
- ○ understand
- ○ coral

4 Is that _____ coming from a snake?

- ○ color
- ● rattle
- ○ desert

5 Mark cut his hand on a _____ of mirror.

- ● sliver
- ○ apple
- ○ finger

Common Core State Standards

Questions 1–5: CCSS Language 4. Determine or clarify the meaning of unknown and multiple-meaning words and phrases based on *grade 2 reading and content*, choosing flexibly from an array of strategies.

PHONICS

Directions

Read each sentence. Fill in the circle next to the answer that has the same syllable pattern as the underlined word.

6 What is in the <u>basket</u>?
- ● monkey
- ○ grape
- ○ baby

7 Our doctor likes to talk about <u>baseball</u>.
- ○ driver
- ● rabbit
- ○ over

8 Let's visit the <u>tiger</u> at the zoo.
- ○ witness
- ● comet
- ○ speed

9 Eat your <u>oatmeal</u>.
- ○ passport
- ● coatroom
- ○ opening

10 Did you hit the <u>target</u>?
- ○ paper
- ○ sprayers
- ● flatter

GO ON

Common Core State Standards

Questions 6–7, 10: **CCSS Foundational Skills 3.** Know and apply grade-level phonics and word analysis skills in decoding words.
Questions 8–9: **CCSS Foundational Skills 3.c.** Decode regularly spelled two-syllable words with long vowels.

Name _____

COMPREHENSION

Late!

Sue sat up in bed. The clock read almost eight.

She raced around her room. "I just cannot be late!"

Her socks were in the window. Her shirt was on the floor.

Her pants were on the chair. One shoe was by the door.

She got dressed very quickly but still had more to do.

Then down under her bed, she found her other shoe.

She opened the front door, but it had been too long.

No one else was waiting. The bus had come and gone!

She went to see her parents and ran right back inside.

She told her mom what happened, and how she'd really tried.

"Please, you need to hurry—I missed the bus today!"

Her mother laughed and smiled, "Today is Saturday!"

Directions

Read each question. Fill in the circle next to the answer.

11 Where was Sue at the beginning of the poem?

- ○ eating breakfast
- ○ at her computer
- ● in bed

12 Why is she racing around her room?

- ○ She's cleaning her room really fast.
- ○ She can't remember where her backpack is.
- ● She thinks she is late for school.

13 What does Sue see when she opens the front door?

- ● no one at the bus stop
- ○ some kids playing soccer
- ○ that it's snowing outside

14 What does Sue learn from her mom?

- ○ Her mother can't take her to school.
- ○ She will have to walk.
- ● It's Saturday.

15 What lesson did Sue learn?

- ○ to get to school on time every day
- ● to remember what day of the week it is
- ○ to pay careful attention to her mother

GO ON

Common Core State Standards

Questions 11–14: CCSS Literature 1. Ask and answer such questions as *who, what, where, when, why,* and *how* to demonstrate understanding of key details in a text. **Question 15: CCSS Literature 2.** Recount stories, including fables and folktales from diverse cultures, and determine their central message, lesson, or moral.

Name _____

WRITTEN RESPONSE TO THE SELECTION

Look Back and Write Look back at pages 136–138. What do the little fish do to help Luna return to the sky? Provide evidence to support your answer.

Use the list in the box below to help you as you write.

REMEMBER — YOU SHOULD

- [ ] tell what the little fish do to help Luna return to the sky.

- [ ] use details from the story to support your answer.

- [ ] write your sentences in an order that makes sense to the reader.

- [ ] try to use correct spelling, capitalization, punctuation, grammar, and sentences.

GO ON

Common Core State Standards

CCSS Literature 3. Describe how characters in a story respond to major events and challenges. (Also **CCSS Literature 1.**, **CCSS Literature 2.**, **CCSS Language 1.**, **CCSS Language 2.**, **CCSS Language 3.**)

Name _____

VOCABULARY

Directions
Read each sentence. Fill in the circle next to the word that fills the blank.

1 Mom will _____ at 6:00 in the morning.

- ○ working
- ○ probably
- ● awaken

2 When the _____ erupted, fire and smoke went up into the air.

- ● volcano
- ○ storm
- ○ ocean

3 The _____ were very steep and rocky.

- ○ sofas
- ● cliffs
- ○ rivers

4 No one likes to _____ with a cold.

- ○ alone
- ● suffer
- ○ hungry

5 Dad saw a _____ after the thunderstorm.

- ● rainbow
- ○ sunshine
- ○ morning

GO ON

Common Core State Standards

Questions 1–5: CCSS Language 4.a. Use sentence-level context as a clue to the meaning of a word or phrase.

PHONICS

Directions

Read each sentence and the question that follows it. Fill in the circle next to the answer.

6 We eat soup with a <u>spoon</u>.

Which word has the same sound as the <u>oo</u> as in <u>spoon</u>?

● view
○ door
○ sour

7 Gary watches the <u>news</u> on TV.

Which word has the same sound as <u>ew</u> in <u>news</u>?

○ Monday
○ Wednesday
● Tuesday

8 I like beets. It's <u>true</u>!

Which word has the same sound as the <u>ue</u> in <u>true</u>?

○ bush
○ gum
● blew

9 The geese <u>flew</u> south for the winter.

Which word has the same sound as the <u>ew</u> in <u>flew</u>?

○ look
● school
○ how

10 The harvest <u>moon</u> is big and bright.

Which word has the same sound as the <u>oo</u> in <u>moon</u>?

○ wood
○ floor
● glue

GO ON

Common Core State Standards

Questions 6–10: CCSS Foundational Skills 3.b. Know spelling-sound correspondences for additional common vowel teams.

Name _____

COMPREHENSION

Up, Up, and Away!

Rick and Tim were brothers. One day their Dad asked, "Do you want to go for a ride in a hot air balloon?"

Rick and Tim said yes. They were excited because they had never been in a balloon before. Dad drove them to a large field where they saw the balloon. It was huge and decorated with many different colors. Dad helped Rick and Tim climb into the balloon's basket. Then he sat down in a special seat next to the controls.

"Hold on!" Dad said. There was a loud noise, and the balloon started to rise. "Up, up, and away!" Dad shouted.

Soon they were close to the clouds. Rick and Tim could not believe what they were seeing. Everything on the ground looked so small! Trees looked like sticks. Cars looked like ants. Rick and Tim looked at each other and smiled. This was so much fun!

The best part of this ride is having you boys up here with me," Dad said to Rick and Tim. "I am very lucky to have boys like you." Rick and Tim smiled. Dad worked very hard, and they did not get to spend much time with him. But the time they did spend with him was special.

Dad pointed down at a tiny purple speck. "That's our home!" he told the boys. "How can you tell?" Rick and Tim asked Dad.

"The roof is purple," Dad told them. "I painted it that color so we could see it from the balloon!"

GO ON

Directions

Read each question. Fill in the circle next to the best answer.

11 What does Dad use to take Rick and Tim for a ride?

- ○ a race car
- ● a hot air balloon
- ○ an airplane

12 A theme of this story is

- ○ balloon rides are scary.
- ● fathers spending time with sons.
- ○ painting the roof of your home.

13 What is Dad's favorite part of the balloon ride?

- ● spending time with Rick and Tim
- ○ seeing their home
- ○ seeing their car

14 What do Rick and Tim learn about Dad?

- ○ Dad cares about balloons.
- ○ Dad cares about their home.
- ● Dad cares about them.

15 What does Dad show Rick and Tim from the balloon?

- ● the roof of their home
- ○ the roof of their car
- ○ He does not show them anything.

GO ON

Common Core State Standards

Questions 11, 13–15: CCSS Literature 1. Ask and answer such questions as *who, what, where, when, why,* and *how* to demonstrate understanding of key details in a text. **Question 12: CCSS Literature 2.** Recount stories, including fables and folktales from diverse cultures, and determine their central message, lesson, or moral.

Name _____

WRITTEN RESPONSE TO THE SELECTION

> **Look Back and Write** Look back at page 169. Do you think Jade is brave? Provide evidence to support your answer.

Use the list in the box below to help you as you write.

REMEMBER — YOU SHOULD

- ☐ tell whether or not you think Jade is brave.

- ☐ use words that describe what Jade does and how she behaves.

- ☐ use details from the story to support your answer.

- ☐ try to use correct spelling, capitalization, punctuation, grammar, and sentences.

GO ON

Common Core State Standards

CCSS Writing 1. Write opinion pieces in which they introduce the topic or book they are writing about, state an opinion, supply reasons that support the opinion, use linking words (e.g., *because, and, also*) to connect opinion and reasons, and provide a concluding statement or section. (Also **CCSS Literature 2., CCSS Literature 7., CCSS Language 1., CCSS Language 2., CCSS Language 3.**)

Name _____

VOCABULARY

Directions
Read each sentence. Fill in the circle next to the word that fills the blank.

1 I will meet you at the train _____.
- ○ piece
- ● station
- ○ apple

2 They are _____ a new school for us.
- ● building
- ○ there
- ○ everybody

3 With a loud _____, the lion stood in front of the cave.
- ○ burning
- ○ meat
- ● roar

4 If you dress _____, we'll have more time to play.
- ● quickly
- ○ please
- ○ masks

5 My little sister always holds my hand _____.
- ○ loud
- ○ myself
- ● tightly

Common Core State Standards

Questions 1–5: CCSS Language 4.a. Use sentence-level context as a clue to the meaning of a word or phrase.

PHONICS

Directions
Read each sentence. Fill in the circle next to the word that fills in the blank.

6 I _____ went with my brother to the movies.

- ○ happiful
- ○ happier
- ● happily

7 Sunsets are _____.

- ○ beautier
- ● beautiful
- ○ beautyish

8 Matt wants to be a _____ in the choir.

- ● singer
- ○ sing
- ○ singly

9 There are _____ people in school today than there were yesterday.

- ○ fewly
- ○ few
- ● fewer

10 Over the holidays we had lots of _____.

- ○ visitfuls
- ● visitors
- ○ visitly

GO ON

Common Core State Standards

Questions 6–10: CCSS Foundational Skills 3.d. Decode words with common prefixes and suffixes.

Name _____

COMPREHENSION

Firefighters

Firefighters are people who have learned how to put out fires. They go through special training to learn this. Some firefighters are volunteers. For others it is their career, or job. There are about one million firefighters in the United States.

Firefighters do three main things when they are putting out a fire. They save people's lives. They try to save people's houses and things. They also try to protect the other houses and trees around the fire. Fires that burn trees in the forest are called wildfires. They are worse than other fires. They are very hard for firefighters to fight because they spread very fast.

Firefighters are much braver than other people. They are also rescue workers. They help when there is a car crash. They help when people get trapped. Some firefighters also have medical training, so they can do some things that doctors or nurses do. This can save people's lives.

One of the most important things firefighters must do is keep themselves safe. Firefighters often work in pairs when they are in a dangerous situation. They also wear alarms that will go off if they stop moving. This way, other firefighters can find them and get them outside to safety.

Being a firefighter is harder than other jobs. It can be very dangerous. But it is a very important job. Firefighters save lives and make all of us a little safer.

GO ON

Directions

Read each question. Fill in the circle next to the best answer.

11 Which is a fact from paragraph 1?

- ○ Firefighters try to save people's houses and things.
- ○ Another way firefighters keep themselves safe is by practicing.
- ● There are about one million firefighters in the United States.

12 Which is an opinion from paragraph 2?

- ○ Fires that burn in the forest are called wildfires.
- ● Wildfires are worse than other fires.
- ○ Firefighers do more than put out fires.

13 Which is an opinion from paragraph 3?

- ● Firefighters are much braver than other people.
- ○ Firefighters help when there is a car crash.
- ○ Some firefighters have medical training.

14 Which is a fact from paragraph 4?

- ○ Being a firefighter is dangerous.
- ○ Being a firefighter is harder than other jobs.
- ● Firefighters wear alarms that go off if they stop moving.

15 Which is an opinion from the passage?

- ● Being a firefighter is harder than other jobs.
- ○ Firefighters often work in pairs.
- ○ Some firefighters are volunteers.

GO ON

/ **Common Core State Standards**

Questions 11–15: CCSS Informational Text 1. Ask and answer such questions as *who, what, where, when, why,* and *how* to demonstrate understanding of key details in a text.

Name _____

WRITTEN RESPONSE TO THE SELECTION

Look Back and Write Look back at page 207. Are the firefighters careful as they search for Luke? How do you know this is not a fictional story? Provide evidence to support your answer.

Use the list in the box below to help you as you write.

REMEMBER—YOU SHOULD

☐   tell if the firefighters are careful as they search for Luke and explain how you know this is not a fictional story.

☐   use details from the text to support your answer.

☐   explain what makes a story fictional to the reader.

☐   try to use correct spelling, capitalization, punctuation, grammar, and sentences.

GO ON

Common Core State Standards

CCSS Informational Text 6. Identify the main purpose of a text, including what the author wants to answer, explain, or describe. (Also **CCSS Writing 5.**, **CCSS Language 1.**, **CCSS Language 2.**)

Name _____

VOCABULARY

Directions

Read each sentence. Fill in the circle next to the word that fills the blank.

1 When you sign your name, that's your _____.

- ○ hand
- ● signature
- ○ pen

2 When my brother doesn't know what to say, he just _____.

- ● shrugs
- ○ jumps
- ○ slowly

3 I had to _____ about the test. It was unfair!

- ● complain
- ○ mumbles
- ○ help

4 Let's meet in the afternoon at 2 _____.

- ○ A.M.
- ○ day
- ● P.M.

5 Have you ever done something just to _____ someone?

- ○ sorry
- ● annoy
- ○ drop

Common Core State Standards

Questions 1–5: CCSS Language 4.a. Use sentence-level context as a clue to the meaning of a word or phrase.

PHONICS

Directions

Read each sentence. Fill in the circle next to the word that fills the blank.

6 I was in such a hurry this morning, I left my bed _____.

- ○ remade
- ● unmade
- ○ premade

7 I _____ my shoes when I want to take them off.

- ○ distie
- ○ retie
- ● untie

8 Since I lost my worksheet, I had to _____ it.

- ● redo
- ○ predo
- ○ undo

9 I had to _____ my food because it became cold.

- ○ preheat
- ○ unheat
- ● reheat

10 I _____ it when people are mean to each other.

- ○ unlike
- ○ prelike
- ● dislike

GO ON

Common Core State Standards

Questions 6–10: **CCSS Foundational Skills 3.d.** Decode words with common prefixes and suffixes.

COMPREHENSION

How to Make Cut Cookies

Cut cookies are fun to make. You get to decorate them after they are baked. To make cut cookies, you will need sugar cookie dough, cookie cutters, a rolling pin, baking sheets, a place to let the cookies cool, and frosting and sugar for decorating.

The first thing you do is make the cookie dough. Then put it in the fridge for an hour or two.

When you are ready to cut out the cookies, preheat your oven. Sprinkle some flour on a clean counter. Then roll out the dough with a rolling pin.

Dip your cookie cutters in flour to help stop sticking. Then press them down into the dough. Cut as many cookies as you can with the dough. Then lay them on a baking sheet. Bake the cookies for eight to ten minutes. Then place them on waxed paper to cool.

After the cookies are cooled, get out your frosting and decorations. Put a thin layer of frosting on a cookie. Then decorate it right away before the frosting dries. Use lots of colors and designs. Have fun! Be creative!

When you are all done decorating, put the cookies away and clean up. The last thing you do is eat the cookies! Yum!

Directions

Read each question. Fill in the circle next to the best answer.

11 What happens when you put the cookie dough in the fridge?

- ○ The cookie dough gets soft.
- ● The cookie dough gets cold.
- ○ The cookie dough mixes together.

12 Why do you use a rolling pin?

- ● to make the dough thin and even
- ○ to warm up the dough after its been in the fridge
- ○ to keep your fingers and the counter clean

13 Why do you dip the cookie cutters in flour?

- ○ to cool them off
- ● to keep the dough from sticking
- ○ to make the cookies prettier

14 What happens to the cookies in the oven?

- ○ The cookies get frosted.
- ○ The cookies cool off.
- ● The cookies bake.

15 Why do you decorate the cookies before the frosting dries?

- ● to make sure the decorations stick
- ○ to make sure the decorations are bright
- ○ to make sure the cookies taste good

GO ON

Common Core State Standards

Questions 11–15: CCSS Informational Text 1. Ask and answer such questions as *who, what, where, when, why,* and *how* to demonstrate understanding of key details in a text.

Name _____

WRITTEN RESPONSE TO THE SELECTION

Look Back and Write Look back at page 236. What does the petition ask for? Use evidence to support your answer.

Use the list in the box below to help you as you write.

REMEMBER—YOU SHOULD

☐ explain what the petition asks for.

☐ tell who writes the petition and to whom they write the petition.

☐ use details from the story to support your answer.

☐ try to use correct spelling, capitalization, punctuation, grammar, and sentences.

GO ON

Common Core State Standards

CCSS Literature 1. Ask and answer such questions as *who, what, where, when, why,* and *how* to demonstrate understanding of key details in a text. (Also **CCSS Writing 5., CCSS Language 1., CCSS Language 2.**)

Name _____

VOCABULARY

Directions

Read each sentence. Fill in the circle next to the word that fills the blank.

1 I _____ the piano every day.
- ○ bottle
- ○ treat
- ● practice

2 Jon is _____ bubble gum.
- ● chewing
- ○ moving
- ○ roaring

3 My dog _____ me as I ran around the yard.
- ○ barked
- ○ poured
- ● chased

4 The lamb _____ its tail as it ate.
- ● wagged
- ○ grabbed
- ○ yelled

5 I was _____ wet from walking home in the rain.
- ○ running
- ○ swimming
- ● dripping

GO ON

Common Core State Standards

Questions 1–5: CCSS Language 4. Determine or clarify the meaning of unknown and multiple-meaning words and phrases based on *grade 2 reading and content*, choosing flexibly from an array of strategies.

PHONICS

Directions

Read each sentence and the question that follows it. Fill in the circle next to the answer.

6 I read the <u>sign</u> on the door.

Which word has the same sound as <u>gn</u> in <u>sign</u>?

- ● gnat
- ○ signature
- ○ song

7 She tied a <u>knot</u> in the rope.

Which word has the same sound as <u>kn</u> in <u>knot</u>?

- ○ ink
- ● knee
- ○ sank

8 I like <u>writing</u> poems in my journal.

Which word has the same sound as <u>wr</u> in <u>writing</u>?

- ○ who
- ○ weather
- ● wrong

9 The <u>lambs</u> were born in late winter.

Which word has the same sound as <u>mb</u> in <u>lambs</u>?

- ● comb
- ○ labs
- ○ damp

10 My mom taught me how to <u>knit</u>.

Which word has the same sound as <u>kn</u> in <u>knit</u>?

- ○ kiss
- ○ kit
- ● knife

GO ON

Common Core State Standards

Questions 6–10: CCSS Foundational Skills 3. Know and apply grade-level phonics and word analysis skills in decoding words.

Name _____

COMPREHENSION

Carmen the Responsible

"Mom! Can we get a dog?" Carmen yelled as she rushed in the door. She had just gotten home from school. "Can we, Mom?"

Mom looked at Carmen for a moment. "Who will take care of the dog?" she asked at last.

"I will!" Carmen said. She smiled big, hoping her mom would say yes. But her mom was not sure. "Let me think about it," she said and went back to working on the computer.

Carmen went into her room. *I really want a dog,* she thought. *How can I show Mom that I can take care of it?* She thought and thought. Then she had an idea. *I'll show her I can be responsible so she'll see that I can take care of a dog.*

The first thing Carmen did was clean up her room. She knew her mom would be happy that she did it all on her own. Then she went to the living room and picked up. Her mom looked surprised when she came out of her office later. "Wow, it looks wonderful out here," she said. "Thanks, Carmen." But she didn't say anything about a dog.

All the next week Carmen helped take care of the house, doing what she could. She didn't wait for her mom to ask her for help. She helped when she saw something that needed to be done.

When Carmen found out her next door neighbor had hurt his knee, she offered to walk his dog, Scruffy. She got up extra early and walked Scruffy in the morning. Then she made sure he had water and food. She walked him when she got home from school, and then again after dinner.

A few days later Mom said to Carmen, "You have worked really hard to take care of Scruffy this past week. You have also helped out so much around here. You've been very responsible. I think we should get a dog." Carmen jumped up and down because she was so happy. Then she ran over and gave her mom a huge hug.

GO ON

Directions

Read each question. Fill in the circle next to the best answer.

11 **How does this story begin?**

● Carmen asks Mom for something.

○ Carmen tells Mom some big news.

○ Mom brings Carmen a surprise.

12 **What does Carmen want?**

● a dog of her own

○ to visit her neighbors

○ to be a dog walker

13 **How does Carmen show her mom that she can take care of a dog?**

○ She does all her homework.

○ She earns her own money.

● She helps her mom and a neighbor.

14 **How does Carmen help her neighbor?**

○ She cleans his house too.

● She walks his dog, Scruffy.

○ She takes him to the doctor.

15 **What is the theme of this story?**

○ Moms are always right.

○ You should do what your mom tells you to do.

● Helping people and being responsible helps you.

2 Copyright © Pearson Education, Inc., or its affiliates. All Rights Reserved.

GO ON

Common Core State Standards

Questions 11–14: **CCSS Literature 1.** Ask and answer such questions as *who, what, where, when, why,* and *how* to demonstrate understanding of key details in a text. **Question 15: CCSS Literature 2.** Recount stories, including fables and folktales from diverse cultures, and determine their central message, lesson, or moral.

Name _____

WRITTEN RESPONSE TO THE SELECTION

Look Back and Write Look back at pages 273–274. What does Sam compare Dodger's training to? Provide evidence to support your answer.

Use the list in the box below to help you as you write.

REMEMBER—YOU SHOULD

☐ tell what Sam compares Dodger's training to.

☐ tell whether you think the comparison is good or not.

☐ write your answer neatly so the reader can understand what you are saying.

☐ try to use correct spelling, capitalization, punctuation, grammar, and sentences.

GO ON

Common Core State Standards

CCSS Literature 1. Ask and answer such questions as *who, what, where, when, why,* and *how* to demonstrate understanding of key details in a text. (Also **CCSS Writing 5., CCSS Language 1., CCSS Language 2.**)

Name _____

VOCABULARY

Directions
Read each sentence. Fill in the circle next to the word that fills the blank.

1 Hiking can be a real _____.

- ○ sound
- ● adventure
- ○ clubhouse

2 Julia _____ the big tree.

- ○ wondered
- ○ chased
- ● climbed

3 My team played the _____ game!

- ○ tomorrow
- ○ finish
- ● greatest

4 People are still _____ outer space.

- ○ chewing
- ○ thinking
- ● exploring

5 Danny is my _____ friend.

- ● truest
- ○ front
- ○ been

Common Core State Standards

Questions 1–5: CCSS Language 4. Determine or clarify the meaning of unknown and multiple-meaning words and phrases based on *grade 2 reading and content*, choosing flexibly from an array of strategies.

- -

PHONICS

Directions
Find the word that has the same sound as the underlined letters in the first word. Fill in the circle next to the answer.

6 ba<u>ng</u>
- ○ taught
- ○ goat
- ● song

7 <u>ph</u>one
- ○ pony
- ○ gone
- ● fire

8 <u>s</u>ick
- ○ alphabet
- ● kiss
- ○ tooth

9 si<u>ng</u>
- ● rang
- ○ gold
- ○ couch

10 gra<u>ph</u>
- ○ grape
- ○ gap
- ● leaf

GO ON

Common Core State Standards

Questions 6–10: **CCSS Foundational Skills 3.** Know and apply grade-level phonics and word analysis skills in decoding words.

Name _____

COMPREHENSION

Blue Jay Saturday

Steve and Alex wanted to raise money for their Little League baseball team, which was named the Blue Jays. But they didn't know how. "What should we do?" Steve asked.

"I have an idea," Alex said. "Let's set up tables in City Park and sell pictures of the team and baseball cards with the players on them. We can have other tables too. They can sell cakes shaped like baseballs and bats."

"That's a terrific idea!" Steve said. "We'll call it the Baseball Market!"

Besides the sale, Steve and Alex made sure that there were many other activities at the Baseball Market. Many people took pony rides around the park. Some people ate hot dogs under the trees. Other people lay on the grass and took in the sun.

The day was beautiful. There were no clouds. The weather was warm for September. The sky was blue. "The color of blue jays," Steve said.

Many more people came to the market than the boys expected. "We sold more than 400 tickets!" Alex told Steve at the end of the day.

"It must be because of the nice weather," Steve said.

As the boys were cleaning up, the coach of the Blue Jays said to them, "I'm very thankful for your help. Now we can get new balls and new bats."

Steve and Alex smiled at the coach. "We're glad that the Baseball Market was such a big hit!" they said to him.

GO ON

Directions

Read each question. Fill in the circle next to the best answer.

11 Why do Steve and Alex set up the Baseball Market?

○ because they like baseball

● to raise money for the Blue Jays

○ because they like their baseball coach

12 Where does the Baseball Market take place?

● City Park

○ at school

○ on a baseball field

13 Why do Steve and Alex plan other activities for the Baseball Market?

● to get more people to come

○ to make sure there are things to do even in bad weather

○ because the coach tells them to

14 How does the weather on Saturday add to the setting of the story?

○ It helps explain why people ate hot dogs.

○ It helps explain why September is a beautiful month.

● It helps explain why so many people came to the market.

15 Why are Steve and Alex happy at the end of the story?

● because the Baseball Market was a success

○ because it was a beautiful day

○ because they took pony rides around City Park

GO ON

Common Core State Standards

Questions 11, 13, 15: CCSS Literature 3. Describe how characters in a story respond to major events and challenges. **Questions 12, 14: CCSS Literature 1.** Ask and answer such questions as *who, what, where, when, why,* and *how* to demonstrate understanding of key details in a text.

WRITTEN RESPONSE TO THE SELECTION

> **Look Back and Write** Look back at page 306. Why does Dolores change her mind about the clubhouse? Provide evidence to support your answer.

Use the list in the box below to help you as you write.

REMEMBER—YOU SHOULD

☐ explain why Dolores changes her mind about the clubhouse.

☐ give at least two reasons for Dolores's decision.

☐ use details from the story to support your answer.

☐ try to use correct spelling, capitalization, punctuation, grammar, and sentences.

GO ON

Common Core State Standards

CCSS Literature 1. Ask and answer such questions as *who, what, where, when, why,* and *how* to demonstrate understanding of key details in a text. (Also **CCSS Writing 5., CCSS Language 1., CCSS Language 2.**)

Name _____

VOCABULARY

Directions
Read each sentence. Fill in the circle next to the word that fills the blank.

1 Halley came up with four good _____ for a class project.

- ○ tables
- ● ideas
- ○ teachers

2 I have a very _____ test today.

- ○ second
- ○ science
- ● important

3 You can't _____ her for your mistake.

- ○ sorry
- ○ ask
- ● blame

4 The _____ had a parade.

- ● townspeople
- ○ everywhere
- ○ birthday

5 Let's play a game this _____.

- ○ note
- ● afternoon
- ○ black

GO ON

Common Core State Standards
Questions 1–5: CCSS Language 4.a. Use sentence-level context as a clue to the meaning of a word or phrase.

PHONICS

Directions

Read each sentence. Fill in the circle next to the word with the /au/ sound that fills the blank.

6 The class has run out of _____.

- ● chalk
- ○ fans
- ○ students

7 _____ is Beth's favorite thing.

- ○ Cake
- ● Autumn
- ○ Math

8 Giselle _____ me to play soccer.

- ○ made
- ○ asked
- ● taught

9 The picnic will be held on the _____.

- ○ grass
- ● lawn
- ○ floor

10 Tim _____ both fish.

- ○ dropped
- ● caught
- ○ ate

GO ON

2 Copyright © Pearson Education, Inc., or its affiliates. All Rights Reserved.

Common Core State Standards

Questions 6–10: CCSS Foundational Skills 3.b. Know spelling-sound correspondences for additional common vowel teams.

Name _____

COMPREHENSION

Rock and Roll

How do you form a rock band?

Two brothers, Bob and Scott Dupre, found the answer. "I play guitar," Bob says. "And Scott sings. So we needed a drummer and a bass player."

Once they found the other players, the group met every day after school.

Bob came up with sounds on the guitar. Scott wrote the words he would sing. The drummer came up with a beat. Then the bass player wrote his part. "Next thing we knew, we had a song," Scott says.

The Beatles, one of the most successful rock bands ever, were a good example for the brothers. The Beatles got together in Liverpool, England, in the 1950s. They were friends who liked music and liked to write songs together.

Writing songs was easy. The hardest part was coming up with a name for the band. "Finally, we just used our own name. The Dupre Brothers," Bob says.

Directions

Read each question. Fill in the circle next to the best answer.

11 What do you need most when you form a rock band?

- ○ garage
- ● players
- ○ sounds

12 What is the main idea of paragraph 4?

- ● The players come up with a song.
- ○ The players practice in the garage.
- ○ Scott wrote the words to sing.

13 What is the most important idea of paragraph 5?

- ○ The Beatles got together in Liverpool.
- ● The Beatles set a good example.
- ○ The Beatles were good friends.

14 What is the main idea of paragraph 6?

- ● Coming up with a name for the band was hard.
- ○ Writing songs is fun for the Dupre brothers.
- ○ The players couldn't pick a name for the band.

15 What is the selection all about?

- ○ The Beatles
- ○ music
- ● forming a rock band

GO ON

Common Core State Standards

Questions 11–15: CCSS Informational Text 2. Identify the main topic of a multiparagraph text as well as the focus of specific paragraphs within the text.

WRITTEN RESPONSE TO THE SELECTION

Look Back and Write Look back at page 346. How does Norman fix the problems he caused? Provide evidence to support your answer.

Use the list in the box below to help you as you write.

REMEMBER—YOU SHOULD

☐ tell how Norman fixes the problems he caused.

☐ make sure you explain the problems Norman caused before telling how he fixes them.

☐ use details from the story to support your answer.

☐ try to use correct spelling, capitalization, punctuation, grammar, and sentences.

GO ON

Common Core State Standards

CCSS Literature 1. Ask and answer such questions as *who, what, where, when, why,* and *how* to demonstrate understanding of key details in a text. (Also **CCSS Writing 5., CCSS Language 1., CCSS Language 2.**)

Name _____

Josh Gibson

VOCABULARY

Directions

Read each sentence. Fill in the circle next to the word that fills the blank.

1 The crowd always _____ for our team.

- ○ beans
- ● cheers
- ○ insects

2 I _____ the ball to Kara.

- ● threw
- ○ broke
- ○ field

3 The boat _____ on the water.

- ○ felt
- ● sailed
- ○ walked

4 Emma ran to home _____ during the game.

- ○ sheep
- ○ joking
- ● plate

5 There were players at all of the _____.

- ○ glasses
- ○ trains
- ● bases

Common Core State Standards

Questions 1–5: CCSS Language 4.a. Use sentence-level context as a clue to the meaning of a word or phrase.

PHONICS

Directions

Read each sentence. Choose the correct ending for the underlined word. Fill in the circle next to the answer.

6 We <u>walking</u> to the store.
- ● walked
- ○ walks
- ○ walker

7 Ashley is the <u>talls</u> person in my class.
- ○ talling
- ● tallest
- ○ talled

8 Jason <u>like</u> to play outside.
- ● likes
- ○ liking
- ○ likest

9 Mrs. Jones <u>teaching</u> us every day.
- ○ teacher
- ○ teachs
- ● teaches

10 We have got to study <u>hards</u>.
- ○ harding
- ● harder
- ○ harded

2 Copyright © Pearson Education, Inc., or its affiliates. All Rights Reserved.

GO ON

Common Core State Standards

Questions 6–10: Foundational Skills 3.d. Decode words with common prefixes and suffixes.

Name _____

COMPREHENSION

A Day of Sweetness and Light

Mary and Juan Almaredo own the Sweetness and Light Bakery in San Diego. They work together, but they have very different jobs.

Mary gets to work at four o'clock in the morning. She has to start so early because she has to make all the breads and rolls. Breads and rolls take a lot of time because they have to rise before baking.

"That's the light part of the bakery," Mary says. "Bread has to get air into it so that it becomes light and soft."

Juan comes at six o'clock to open the store. He hangs the sign, sets up the chairs, and cleans the cases. Then he unlocks the front door.

The smell of fresh baked goods reaches far down the block. Customers pour into the store for their treats.

Once the store is open, Juan goes to the kitchen, and Mary takes her place at the counter. All day she helps customers. She takes orders, wraps breads and sweets, and makes change when customers pay. Customers love her smile and her happy way.

Juan, meanwhile, makes cakes. Customers order them for birthdays and other celebrations. He also makes brownies and cookies. "I use lots of sugar every day," he says. "That's the sweetness part of the bakery."

At the end of the day, Mary and Juan lock the door of the bakery. They sweep and mop the floor. They wash the dishes and turn out the lights.

They are tired, but it was another day of sweetness and light.

GO ON

Directions

Read each question. Fill in the circle next to the best answer.

11 **How are Mary and Juan alike?**

- ● They both work at a bakery.
- ○ They both get to work at four o'clock.
- ○ They both make a lot of money.

12 **How are Mary and Juan different?**

- ● Mary and Juan go to work at different times.
- ○ Juan is a sweeter person than Mary.
- ○ Mary and Juan leave work at different times.

13 **Which of the following statements is true?**

- ○ Mary buys all the supplies, and Juan uses them.
- ○ Mary makes messes, and Juan cleans them up.
- ● When Juan starts working in the kitchen, Mary works at the counter.

14 **One way that Juan and Mary are the same is**

- ○ they fight over who gets to help the customers.
- ○ they both take the customers' orders.
- ● they work together to clean at the end of the day.

15 **Which of the following is NOT a difference between Mary and Juan?**

- ○ Mary starts work at four in the morning while Juan starts at six.
- ● Mary is nice to all the customers, but Juan yells at them.
- ○ Mary makes breads and rolls, and Juan makes cakes, brownies, and cookies.

GO ON

Common Core State Standards

Questions 11–15: CCSS Literature 3. Describe how characters in a story respond to major events and challenges.

Name _____

WRITTEN RESPONSE TO THE SELECTION

Look Back and Write Look back at page 379. How can a girl play baseball just like Josh Gibson? Provide evidence to support your answer.

Use the list in the box below to help you as you write.

REMEMBER—YOU SHOULD

- [ ] explain how a girl can play baseball just like Josh Gibson.

- [ ] use action words to make your writing more interesting and exciting.

- [ ] use details from the story to support your answer.

- [ ] try to use correct spelling, capitalization, punctuation, grammar, and sentences.

GO ON

Common Core State Standards

CCSS Writing 2. Write informative/explanatory texts in which they introduce a topic, use facts and definitions to develop points, and provide a concluding statement or section. (Also **CCSS Literature 1.**, **CCSS Language 1.**, **CCSS Language 2.**, **CCSS Language 3.**)

Name _____

VOCABULARY

Directions

Read each sentence. Fill in the circle next to the word that fits.

1 Mark gave the little frog its _____.

- ○ pounds
- ● freedom
- ○ birthday

2 There is a _____ in front of the school.

- ● flag
- ○ roof
- ○ great

3 My shirt has blue and white _____.

- ● stripes
- ○ days
- ○ fingers

4 There are many _____ in the sky.

- ○ notes
- ○ masks
- ● stars

5 My friends all have _____.

- ● nicknames
- ○ second
- ○ together

GO ON

Common Core State Standards

Questions 1–5: CCSS Language 4. Determine or clarify the meaning of unknown and multiple-meaning words and phrases based on *grade 2 reading and content*, choosing flexibly from an array of strategies.

WORD ANALYSIS

Directions

Choose the correct abbreviation for each underlined word. Fill in the circle next to the answer.

6 Have you met <u>Mister</u> Allen?
- ● Mr.
- ○ Mtr.
- ○ Msr.

7 I live on Bailey <u>Street</u>.
- ○ Str.
- ○ Sr.
- ● St.

8 Mail the check to <u>Doctor</u> Ruiz.
- ● Dr.
- ○ Do.
- ○ Dc.

9 We don't have school next <u>Tuesday</u>.
- ○ Tu.
- ○ Tue.
- ● Tues.

10 Our address is 202 South Seventh <u>Avenue</u>.
- ○ Aven.
- ● Ave.
- ○ Avn.

GO ON

Common Core State Standards

Questions 6–10: CCSS Language 2. Demonstrate command of the conventions of standard English capitalization, punctuation, and spelling when writing.

Name _____

COMPREHENSION

The State of Texas

Texas is big! It is the second biggest state in size in the United States. Texas has more people living in it than in any other state in our country besides California. In 2006 the population of Texas was 22,859,968.

On December 29, 1845, Texas became the twenty-eighth state to join the United States.

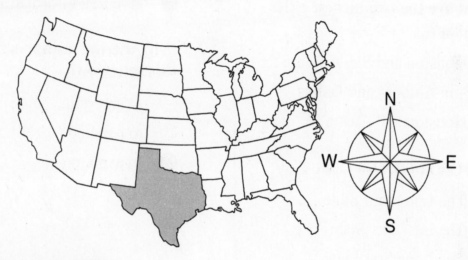

Ten Largest Cities

1.	Houston
2.	San Antonio
3.	Dallas
4.	Austin
5.	Fort Worth
6.	El Paso
7.	Arlington
8.	Corpus Christi
9.	Plano
10.	Garland

State Capital:	Austin
State Abbreviation:	TX
State Bird:	Mockingbird
State Flower:	Bluebonnet
State Nickname:	Lone Star State

GO ON

Directions

Read each question. Fill in the circle next to the best answer.

11 What feature gives information about where Texas is located?

- ○ the paragraphs
- ● the map
- ○ the lists

12 What are the two largest cities in Texas?

- ● Houston and San Antonio
- ○ San Antonio and Dallas
- ○ Houston and Austin

13 What is Texas's nickname?

- ○ The Long Star State
- ○ The Last Star State
- ● The Lone Star State

14 Is the author of this selection trying to make you laugh, make you do something, or give you information?

- ○ make you laugh
- ○ make you do something
- ● give you information

15 Why did the author write this selection?

- ○ to entertain
- ○ to persuade
- ● to explain

GO ON

Common Core State Standards

Questions 11–13: CCSS Informational Text 5. Know and use various text features (e.g., captions, bold print, subheadings, glossaries, indexes, electronic menus, icons) to locate key facts or information in a text quickly and efficiently. **Questions 14–15: CCSS Informational Text 6.** Identify the main purpose of a text, including what the author wants to answer, explain, or describe.

WRITTEN RESPONSE TO THE SELECTION

Look Back and Write Look back at page 409. Why did Frances Scott Key write "The Star-Spangled Banner"? Provide evidence to support your answer.

Use the list in the box below to help you as you write.

REMEMBER — YOU SHOULD

☐ explain why Frances Scott Key wrote "The Star-Spangled Banner."

☐ use words that describe how Frances Scott Key felt.

☐ use details from the text to support your answer.

☐ try to use correct spelling, capitalization, punctuation, grammar, and sentences.

GO ON

Common Core State Standards

CCSS Writing 2. Write informative/explanatory texts in which they introduce a topic, use facts and definitions to develop points, and provide a concluding statement or section. (Also **CCSS Literature 1., CCSS Language 1., CCSS Language 2., CCSS Language 3.**)

Name _____

VOCABULARY

Directions
Read each sentence. Fill in the circle next to the word that fills the blank.

1 I got Mom a _____ for her birthday.
- ○ harvest
- ○ storm
- ● present

2 Julie is visiting her _____.
- ● aunt
- ○ picture
- ○ high

3 Sam put the fruit in a _____.
- ○ trick
- ○ tape
- ● basket

4 Danny _____ baseball cards.
- ○ goes
- ● collects
- ○ trees

5 I got money from the _____.
- ● bank
- ○ after
- ○ half

Common Core State Standards

Questions 1–5: CCSS Language 4.a. Use sentence-level context as a clue to the meaning of a word or phrase.

WORD ANALYSIS

Directions
Fill in the circle next to the word that fills the blank.

6 Jose likes to read _____ stories.

○ ficture
○ fracture
● fiction

7 The _____ of milk and soda pop tasted bad.

○ mature
○ mixer
● mixture

8 Australia is both a _____ and an island.

● nation
○ nature
○ nurture

9 Kids can climb the _____ that is outside the library.

○ sculpting
● sculpture
○ sculptor

10 Use _____ when you cross the street.

○ caucus
● caution
○ cause

Common Core State Standards

Questions 6–10: CCSS Foundational Skills 3. Know and apply grade-level phonics and word analysis skills in decoding words.

Name _____

COMPREHENSION

The California Gold Rush

San Francisco has a football team called the '49ers. Do you know how they got that name? They are named for the year 1849, which is the year the California Gold Rush began.

People from all over the United States and from around the world rushed to California when they heard about lots of gold being found there. These people were said to have a case of "Gold Fever." They expected to become very rich.

The truth is that most of the miners were lucky if they found even ten dollars worth of gold in a day. Some of them got rich, but most were just trying to find enough so that they could buy food.

Thousands of miners died in the years of the Gold Rush. There was a lot of disease and there were many accidents that took their lives.

By the mid-1850s it had become very hard to find any more gold in California. In 1859 silver was discovered in Nevada. The miners went there to try their luck. So ended the California Gold Rush.

Gold Rush Time Line

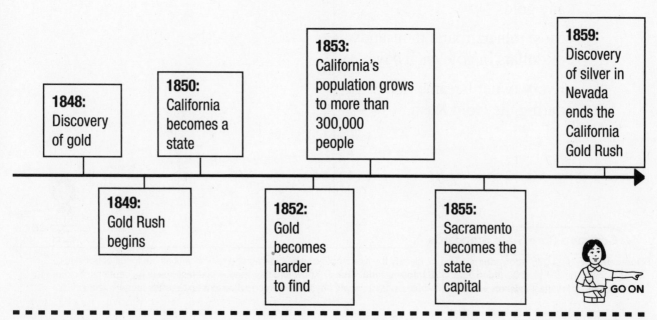

Directions

Read each question. Fill the circle next to the best answer.

11 Why is San Francisco's football team called the '49ers?

- ○ They were named for the year the team was formed.
- ● They were named for the year the Gold Rush began.
- ○ There are 49 players.

12 Was "Gold Fever" a disease?

- ○ Yes, you got it from eating gold.
- ○ Yes, a miner got it when he touched dirty gold.
- ● No, people who hoped to find gold were said to have "Gold Fever."

13 Did most miners become rich?

- ● Most miners found hardly any gold.
- ○ Most miners found thousands of dollars in gold each day.
- ○ Every miner became rich during the Gold Rush.

14 Why did the California Gold Rush end?

- ○ The government ordered it to end.
- ● In 1859 silver was discovered in Nevada, so the miners went there.
- ○ In 1850 California became a state.

15 According to the time line, gold became hard to find in 1852. Why?

- ● So many miners were there that the gold started to run out.
- ○ There was never any gold in California.
- ○ The miners quit looking for gold in 1852.

GO ON

⌐ **Common Core State Standards** ⌐

Questions 11–14: CCSS Informational Text 2. Identify the main topic of a multiparagraph text as well as the focus of specific paragraphs within the text. **Question 15: CCSS Informational Text 5.** Know and use various text features (e.g., captions, bold print, subheadings, glossaries, indexes, electronic menus, icons) to locate key facts or information in a text quickly and efficiently.

2 Copyright © Pearson Education, Inc., or its affiliates. All Rights Reserved.

Name _____

WRITTEN RESPONSE TO THE SELECTION

Look Back and Write Look back at page 440. Why does Cecilia put a flowerpot and a teacup in the basket for Tía? Provide evidence to support your answer.

Use the list in the box below to help you as you write.

REMEMBER — YOU SHOULD

☐   tell why Cecilia puts a flowerpot and a teacup in the basket for Tía.

☐   use words that describe how Cecilia feels about Tía.

☐   use details from the story to support your answer.

☐   try to use correct spelling, capitalization, punctuation, grammar, and sentences.

GO ON

Common Core State Standards

CCSS Writing 2. Write informative/explanatory texts in which they introduce a topic, use facts and definitions to develop points, and provide a concluding statement or section. (Also **CCSS Literature 1., CCSS Language 1., CCSS Language 2., CCSS Language 3.**)

Name _____

VOCABULARY

Directions

Read each sentence. Fill in the circle next to the word that fills the blank.

1 My uncle has _____ on this ranch.

● cattle
○ said
○ coast

2 Sandy walked on the mountain _____.

○ boats
○ ideas
● trails

3 The _____ wore an old brown hat.

● cowboy
○ question
○ block

4 A group of cows is called a _____.

○ dark
● herd
○ galloped

5 We sat next to a warm _____.

○ should
○ turn
● campfire

GO ON

Common Core State Standards

Questions 1–5: CCSS Language 4.a. Use sentence-level context as a clue to the meaning of a word or phrase.

WORD ANALYSIS

Directions

Find the words with the same meaning as the underlined word. Fill in the circle next to the answer.

6 I will not forget your <u>kindness</u> to me.

- ○ being rude
- ● being nice
- ○ being silly

7 The new paint added <u>brightness</u> to the room.

- ○ a light bulb
- ○ being big
- ● having much light

8 Don't be <u>careless</u> when you open that can.

- ● not taking proper care
- ○ being extra careful
- ○ being honest

9 The kitchen was <u>spotless</u> before the party.

- ○ full of food
- ○ having polka dots
- ● fully clean

10 My new dog is <u>fearless</u>.

- ○ afraid of everything
- ● having no fear
- ○ being noisy all the time

GO ON

Common Core State Standards

Questions 6–10: **CCSS Foundational Skills 3.d.** Decode words with common prefixes and suffixes.

Name _____

COMPREHENSION

A Man, A Plan, A Canal—Panama!

The Panama Canal opened in the year 1914. It is a man-made waterway that connects the Pacific and Atlantic oceans. The canal is 50 miles long, and it takes 8 hours to cross it. Every year, more than 14,000 ships use this great shortcut!

Before the Panama Canal was built, ships that were sailing from New York to San Francisco had to go all the way around South America. That trip was 14,000 miles long! By sailing through the canal, that same trip is just 6,000 miles.

Someone had the idea of a canal through Panama in the 1500s, but the first time anyone tried it was in 1880. That plan was led by the French. The United States took over the building of the canal after France lost 22,000 workers. These workers died from disease and accidents.

Working on the Panama Canal was terrible. One worker said, "The mosquitoes get so thick that you get a mouthful with every breath." There were so many insects because of all the muddy water created by cutting down the jungles.

The Panama Canal became very famous. It even has a palindrome. A palindrome is a word or sentence that is spelled the same when read from the front or from the back. Here it is:

A MAN, A PLAN, A CANAL—PANAMA!

GO ON

Directions

Read each question. Fill in the circle next to the best answer.

11 **Which of these happened first?**

- ● Ships had to sail 14,000 miles.
- ○ The French lost 22,000 workers.
- ○ Someone had an idea for a canal.

12 **What happened after the Panama Canal opened in 1914?**

- ○ Workers became very sick.
- ○ Ships began sailing around South America.
- ● The Panama Canal became famous.

13 **What happened before the Panama Canal was built?**

- ○ Ships could not sail from New York to San Francisco.
- ○ Ships only sailed to South America.
- ● Ships sailing from New York to San Francisco had to go around South America.

14 **Which of these happened last?**

- ○ The French worked on the Panama Canal.
- ● The United States worked on the Panama Canal.
- ○ Workers became very sick.

15 **What happened after the workers cut down the jungles?**

- ● The insects got really bad.
- ○ Ships got stuck in the leaves.
- ○ Workers ran out of wood.

GO ON

/ **Common Core State Standards** \

Questions 11–15: CCSS Informational Text 1. Ask and answer such questions as *who, what, where, when, why,* and *how* to demonstrate understanding of key details in a text.

Name _____

WRITTEN RESPONSE TO THE SELECTION

Look Back and Write Look back at page 474. How did hats protect cowboys? Provide evidence to support your answer.

Use the list in the box below to help you as you write.

REMEMBER — YOU SHOULD

☐ tell how hats protected cowboys.

☐ use details from the text to support your answer.

☐ write neatly so that your answer is easy to read.

☐ try to use correct spelling, capitalization, punctuation, grammar, and sentences.

GO ON

Common Core State Standards

CCSS Writing 2. Write informative/explanatory texts in which they introduce a topic, use facts and definitions to develop points, and provide a concluding statement or section. (Also **CCSS Informational Text 1., CCSS Language 1., CCSS Language 2., CCSS Language 3.**)

Name _____

VOCABULARY

Directions
Read each sentence. Fill in the circle next to the word that fills the blank.

1 A good _____ is easy to remember.

- ○ toe
- ● slogan
- ○ there

2 Our school always has _____ before football games.

- ○ balloons
- ○ trials
- ● rallies

3 Did you vote in the _____ ?

- ● election
- ○ yesterday
- ○ official

4 If you use a _____ , people will hear you better.

- ● microphone
- ○ voice
- ○ sentence

5 I don't like to listen to long _____ .

- ○ principals
- ○ wonderful
- ● speeches

Common Core State Standards

Questions 1–5: CCSS Language 4.a. Use sentence-level context as a clue to the meaning of a word or phrase.

WORD ANALYSIS

Directions
Find the word or words with the same meaning as the underlined word. Fill in the circle next to the answer.

6 Don't <u>mistreat</u> your pet.
- ○ treat well
- ○ overfeed
- ● treat badly

7 Don't <u>misplace</u> your pencil before the big test.
- ○ sharpen
- ● lose
- ○ break

8 At <u>midnight</u> my dog howled at the moon.
- ● twelve o'clock at night
- ○ twelve o'clock in the afternoon
- ○ nine o'clock in the evening

9 The ride did a flip in <u>midair</u>.
- ○ clouds that form very high up
- ● part of space above the ground
- ○ section of an airplane near its wings

10 Wendy had to stay after school because of her <u>misbehavior</u>.
- ○ studying hard
- ● behaving badly
- ○ lots of mistakes

GO ON

Common Core State Standards

Questions 6–10: CCSS Foundational Skills 3.d. Decode words with common prefixes and suffixes.

Weekly Test 30 Unit 6 Week 5

Name _____

COMPREHENSION

Amazing Sea Bears

You have never heard of sea bears? Oh, yes you have. The name scientists use for them is Ursus maritimus, or "sea bear." We call Ursus maritimus the polar bear.

Polar bears live in the Arctic, Alaska, Canada, Russia, Greenland, and Norway. All the places they live are very cold and icy.

Polar bears are huge. An adult male can weigh up to 1,500 pounds. Females are much smaller. They weigh between 330 and 650 pounds.

Polar bears' fur is not white. The fur only looks white because it reflects the light. Each hair is hollow, so the fur traps heat. Their fur keeps the bears warm. Because the fur is oily, it keeps their skin dry when they swim.

Polar bears are great swimmers. Their wide front paws and webbed toes help them move in the water. They paddle with their front feet. They steer with their back feet.

Polar bears are predators. They mainly eat seals. The bears wait for seals to come out of the water and then chase them. Or they grab seals swimming under the ice.

Only one animal eats polar bears. Can you guess which animal it is? Correct. People are the polar bear's only predator.

GO ON

Directions

Read each sentence. Fill in the circle next to the best answer.

11 What is another name for a sea bear?

- ○ water bear
- ○ white bear
- ● polar bear

12 What is it like where polar bears live?

- ● icy
- ○ nice
- ○ cool

13 Why does the fur of polar bears look white?

- ○ Their fur is white.
- ○ Their fur is oily.
- ● Their fur reflects light.

14 What part of their body helps polar bears swim?

- ● their paws
- ○ their head
- ○ their teeth

15 What is polar bears' favorite food?

- ○ fish
- ● seals
- ○ snow

GO ON

Common Core State Standards

Questions 11–15: CCSS Informational Text 1. Ask and answer such questions as *who, what, where, when, why,* and *how* to demonstrate understanding of key details in a text.

Name _____

WRITTEN RESPONSE TO THE SELECTION

Look Back and Write Look back at pages 508–509. Why did Grace think becoming president was not going to be easy? Provide evidence to support your answer.

Use the list in the box below to help you as you write.

REMEMBER — YOU SHOULD

☐   tell why Grace thought becoming president was not going to be easy.

☐   describe how Grace felt when she heard Thomas Cobb was going to run for president.

☐   use details from the story to support your answer.

☐   try to use correct spelling, capitalization, punctuation, grammar, and sentences.

GO ON

Common Core State Standards

CCSS Writing 2. Write informative/explanatory texts in which they introduce a topic, use facts and definitions to develop points, and provide a concluding statement or section. (Also **CCSS Literature 1., CCSS Literature 3., CCSS Writing 3., CCSS Language 1., CCSS Language 2., CCSS Language 3.**)

- -

Weekly Test 30 Unit 6 Week 5